THE WOUNDED GET BACK

Books by Albert Q. Maisel

MIRACLES OF MILITARY MEDICINE
AFRICA: FACTS AND FORECASTS

THE WOUNDED GET BACK

by

ALBERT Q. MAISEL

With a foreword by

ROSS T. McINTIRE

REAR ADMIRAL, MEDICAL CORPS, U.S.N.
THE SURGEON GENERAL OF THE NAVY

HARCOURT, BRACE AND COMPANY, NEW YORK

A WARTIME BOOK

*This complete edition is produced in full
compliance with the government's regulations for conserving paper and other
essential materials.*

The author is indebted to many hundreds of Navy doctors, nurses, and corpsmen and to other hundreds of enlisted men and officers of the Navy and the Marine Corps for the countless courtesies—in the giving of aid, advice, and information—which have made this volume possible. He is sure, however, that all these will deem it no slight if he singles out one officer by name and dedicates this book to

ROBERT C. RANSDELL
COMMANDER, MC., USNR

without whose intercession this work could never have been started; without whose counsel it would certainly never have been completed.

Thanks are due to *The Woman's Home Companion* for the use of material in Chapter X, to *Cosmopolitan Magazine* for material in Chapters V and VI, and to the Toronto *Star* for material in Chapters VII and XII.

FOREWORD

FROM Pearl Harbor to the present day, one of the most noteworthy achievements by the Armed Forces has been the conception and maintenance of high standards of medical and hospital care. In the history of warfare more wounded men are recovering and being returned to duty than ever before. The menace of communicable diseases is being reduced by the sound application of preventive medicine. Medical research is being accelerated to the end that scientific knowledge is being applied without delay and thereby plays a great part in saving lives and hastening convalescence.

Mr. Maisel has had an opportunity, such as few laymen ever receive, to observe at firsthand the Navy's Medical Department in action at sea and on land. A discriminating observer, possessing an approach which is both discerning and sympathetic, he portrays the picture in all of its aspects—care of the wounded, preventive medicine, evacuation by ambulance planes, and all of the others.

As a writer accredited by the Navy Department, Mr. Maisel took passage on hospital ships and Navy planes. He talked with bluejackets and marines in rude first-aid stations in the field, and in large, modern hospitals in the rear. He sought and obtained the opinion of apprentice seamen and admirals. His six months in the South Pacific gave him an insight into the workings of Naval medicine which is aptly put to paper in *The Wounded Get Back*.

Americans are entitled to know how their men in uniform

are being cared for when they fall by enemy action or are taken ill. This book, therefore, may be said to contribute a public service.

Ross T. McIntire
Rear Admiral, MC., U.S.N.,
The Surgeon General of the Navy

Washington, D. C.
January 20, 1944

CONTENTS

THE WOUNDED GET BACK

CHAPTER I

THE SEA-GOING CHRISTMAS TREE

I FIRST saw the ship on a rainy winter's day, looking down across the harbor from an office building window. The town was as nondescript as the name I shall be obliged to give it, that wartime evasion called "a North Atlantic Port." The eye wandered easily from the gray roofs below across the gray waters to the equally gray cranes and wharves of the Navy Yard, where ships in battle-paint merged smoothly into the background camouflage which man and nature had combined to provide.

Only my ship stood out in incongruous splendor, a great, gleaming white hull and superstructure, fresh as a twelve-year-old in a new communion dress. On her funnel, a sailor hung in a bosun's chair, putting the finishing touches on a bright red cross. Along her hull, other men were touching up the green line which paralleled the sea and forced the eye towards another great cross amidships.

She was a beautiful thing; as beautiful as the pictures of tropic cruise ships that once graced the pages of peacetime magazines. And as completely out of place as those ships would have been, proposing to sail the gray seas of a world at war.

I turned to Lieutenant Morgan, who had raised the blinds so that I might take in the sight. He read my thoughts.

"The enemy is supposed to have agreed to respect her," he said. "Maybe they will; who knows?"

✦

3

Once on board the *Relief*, I found little of the hospital atmosphere I had anticipated. Instead of the expected quiet, the compartments rang out with the constant, boiler-works clatter of paint chippers. Instead of the respectable odor of iodoform, the nose was greeted by the combined fragrance of varnish, linseed oil, and baked Virginia ham. I had expected the first two, but the last had me stumped until my guide led me, across a maze of air hoses, welding machine wires, and assorted litter, to a long room; windowless and hence less noisy but far more smelly than the open decks.

There, calm in the midst of chaos, were some forty officers, neat in their winter blues, and about as many women, looking equally out of place in their best party dresses. Solemnly, against a background of chipped bulkheads, they lined up on the painters' tarpaulins that covered the floors, each carrying a shining aluminum mess tray. The line led to the end of the room, where half a dozen Negro messmen were calmly and graciously placing ham and hot biscuits and coffee and little cakes upon each passing tray.

"Our farewell supper," my guide explained. "They've painted us out of the wardroom, so we're holding it here in the sick officers' quarters."

We joined the line and then, tray in hand, I experienced for the first time something that was to happen to me, again and again, at every new stop in the Pacific. Instead of interviewing the Navy, as a correspondent should, I found the Navy insisting on first interviewing me.

Yes, I had to explain, I was a correspondent. No, I was not an Army officer. That was just the prescribed uniform for correspondents. Yes, I was going on the voyage. No, I didn't know our destination. Yes, I was going to do a book on Navy Medicine. No, I was not a doctor, just a layman who wrote about medicine.

In the end, Dr. McCarthy rescued me, leading Mrs. Mc-

Carthy and myself out onto the deck. "You mustn't mind their digging," he said. "We've been sitting in one port or another since the war started and those wives have grown used to the idea of seeing their husbands around. Your being sent with us now has set them guessing. If you're going to write a book about us, they figure, it must be a long voyage."

"How do you figure it?" I asked.

It was Mrs. McCarthy who answered. "I hope it's a long trip," she said. Then, noticing my surprise, she added, "I know what you're thinking, Mr. Maisel. But we both hope it's a long trip. We broke up our home a year ago. It's been nice, having Dan here where I could see him and know he was safe. But this is the Doctor's second war. He's got a son in this one. He wants to be where he's needed, where he can do some good. And that's how I want it to be, too."

"My, that's a speech," said the Doctor, trying to hide his pride under words. "I do believe you'll be glad to get rid of me."

Embarrassed, then, we all turned for a last look at the harbor. The city was dark under the blackout, but behind us the welding torches still worked in the busy yard, casting huge shadows that fell away across the black waters. As we leaned against the rail, I could feel the bulge in my pocket where I kept my credentials. Among them was a copy of my basic orders. I was assigned, they said, to the Pacific Fleet, "effective upon ship joining that fleet."

The Doctor would get his wish.

We sailed in the morning. Miraculously, the litter that had covered the decks the night before had disappeared. The noise of the Navy Yard fell away, the city receded and then the coast itself was swallowed up in haze. We had begun a journey that was to keep us out of sight of land, except for one short refueling stop, for the next forty days. We not only traveled unconvoyed. We avoided—literally shunned—other ships, steaming an out-of-the way course that kept us off the more crowded lanes not so much for our own protection as to avoid the danger of our lights serving as a beacon that might guide enemy subs towards the fair game represented by cargo and combat vessels. For protection we had only the promise of the Hague Convention of 1907, a promise which, in the past, had been honored mostly in the breach. We did know that the Japs had, up to then, respected the other white-painted ships we had used in the Pacific, as we had respected their more numerous hospital fleet. So under orders, and with some misgivings, we put our faith in the honor of a foe whose lack of honor had been made manifest, repeatedly, since the first demonstration at Pearl Harbor.

It was only months later that we learned how unfounded our faith had been. I remember listening to the Jap propaganda radio, the "Zero hour," in a small hospital in the Russell Islands. The lisping announcer was denouncing us for sinking a Jap hospital ship, which he did not name. The denunciation made no sense, for I had been shown picture after picture of the Jap Red Cross vessels, pictures taken through the periscopes of our submarines. These photos proved that we had had the opportunity, time and again, to sink such ships. But our pig-boats had refrained—as theirs must have, too—and used cameras instead of torpedoes.

I remarked as much to the officers who were with me. Then one of the men offered his explanation. "I've listened to those birds for a year now, so I think I'm getting on to the way they think. What we're hearing now is the alibi-in-advance. They've either sunk one of our ships or they plan to. And they're washing their hands of the guilt, now, by saying that we started it first."

Within three days our guess was confirmed. On May 10, 1943, a Jap submarine torpedoed the Australian hospital ship,

Centaur, while it was proceeding fully lighted towards New Guinea. More than four-fifths of the personnel aboard, including many nurses, were lost.

But all that was in the future when we sailed. People didn't worry—or, at least, they didn't worry out loud—because the very fact of our steaming along, all white and shiny, showed that no one expected any trouble.

Instead, the crew went about its business of running the ship and chipping paint and cleaning her up. The doctors and nurses busied themselves with small tasks, taking things easy so that the little they had to do would last out the voyage and not leave them with absolutely nothing to do towards the end.

Those first few days at sea, going through the ship's departments one by one on a sort of conducted tour arranged by the medical officers, I found myself often under the illusion of being in some familiar hospital on shore. The great, tile-floored operating room might have been in New York's Bellevue. But then you raised your eyes and saw the porthole-shaped deadlights overhead, covered now for blackout by welded steel sheeting. The dental clinics were as complete as any busy dentist's suite, right down to the diplomas on the wall. But, through the ports, swung open now in the tropic sunlight, you saw ventilators and cargo booms instead of a city street. In the x-ray rooms, you walked on linoleum tiles towards a spectacular examining and fluoroscopy table, the kind that has been streamlined and chromium-finished to impress and intimidate the patient. But instead of the sounds of Park Avenue traffic, the open portholes carried in the swish of passing waters, lapping along the hull.

Down in the large, sixty-bed wards which filled the upper hold, the medical and the nautical merged and mixed in swirls that took the mind off guard. At one moment, in sight of rows of hanging bunks, you were quite certainly on a ship. But if you closed your eyes, the odors—ether, clove, and carbolic—said, unmistakably, "Hospital."

Crowded into spaces between the various wards were numerous other hospital facilities: the special diet kitchens, the great store rooms for linens and medical supplies, and the hundred and one other special service spaces required by any large hospital.

And surrounding all these—above and below and on all sides of the hospital—was the special equipment of a ship designed for long voyages at sea; the pumps and blowers and compressors, the boilers and oil tanks and bilges and engine rooms. Few ships have ever had more paraphernalia crammed within a ten thousand-ton hull. Yet for all that the *Relief* was a roomy—even a gracious—ship with wide decks and infinite passageways.

So many were her nooks and crannies that even an exploring correspondent could not find them all. After weeks at sea, when I thought I had discovered every last surprise upon what the men fondly termed their "bucket," I was astonished one morning to find the winches working and a complete hundred-bed tent-hospital rising from the depths of the quarter-deck hatch. The ship's designers had prepared her for every imaginable contingency including the rather far-fetched possibility of her having so many patients loaded upon her as to necessitate her depositing a portion of the overload in a field hospital on some desert island.

All morning and all afternoon the winches worked, bringing up great cases which the doctors eagerly opened, like pirates breaking into newly captured loot. Out of the cases tumbled demountable dental chairs, operating tables, emergency lighting equipment, and heaven knows what else; each unit a veritable jig-saw puzzle ingeniously designed for compactness.

The only trouble with the ingenious design was that no one except its original designer—long dead, we all hoped—could figure out how to put these marvelous medical gadgets together. For hours the dentists worked on their portable chair only to discover at long length that they had a drill where the head piece ought to be and the spittoon part mounted firmly on the foot rest.

Once we reached port, every one was pretty much relieved when the captain managed to trade off the portable hospital to the local authorities. Undoubtedly much of this equipment has since been put to good use. It couldn't have taken more than a few months for those who inherited it to figure it out.

By the time we had sailed down the east coast and passed through Panama, I felt myself accepted as one of the ship's company. The mass of faces in the officers' wardroom began to separate, first into recognizable groups and then, into individuals. I found myself invited to meals in the nurses' wardroom on the upper deck and with the warrant officers and the "Chiefs" in their quarters on the decks below.

The odds and ends of navy lingo, which I had carefully recorded in my notes the first few days, soon became a part of my own language. I no longer climbed stairs, I mounted "ladders." Ceilings became "overhead," floors were "decks" and walls were "bulkheads." After a time I even ceased to bark my shins on the "coamings," the high steps which one had to remember were at all outer doorways to prevent the sea from running into the ship in rough weather.

The Chiefs' mess proved to be the only one with a truly nautical flavor, for in the Navy, the chief petty officers are the professionals, the men who have risen from the ranks after several enlistments and whose world has a salty smell. After a few days of listening to their endless reminiscences of Cavite, Guam, a place called "Dago" (it proved to be San Diego), Shanghai, Port Arthur, Tripoli, and Guantanimo, I felt that I was among a group of true cosmopolites. It wasn't until several sessions later that I discovered that, whatever the name of the port they were telling about, most of them knew only those things that could be found within sight of the waterfront. Glibly they compared Chinese restaurants in Durban, South Africa, with those to be found in Sydney, Australia. All their stories, about all their girls, their brawls, and their meals, could have been told of any port in the United States.

Yet, if travel had failed to broaden their point of view, it had mellowed their personalities and made them a friendly and infinitely likable group. Their competence was manifest. I soon learned the truth of the old Navy proverb, "If you want to get anything done, see the Chief about it."

Their conversation—to put it mildly—was uninhibited. At meals the standard form for grace was a sentence which can only be approximated—in a book which might fall into the hands of minors—as "Shall we talk about broads right off or shall we lead up to them gradually?" The particular word which they used for women may have varied from time to time, but never was it one that could pass the postal censors.

The nurses' mess was at the other end of the social spectrum. Most of our twelve nurses had never left the States before. A centerpiece of artificial flowers graced *their* table and laughter was held to gentle—and genteel—titters. Before leaving for the war zone, their wardroom had been stripped of its dainty curtains and the figured cretonne slip-covers which had given the room a boarding-school atmosphere. Yet, despite the starkness of its corrugated metal walls, the smell of the sea in the nurses' wardroom was always modified by the feminine odors of perfume and powder. They never griped about the chow on days when the messmen provided Waldorf salad.

Between these extremes, the officers' wardroom reflected the changing character of our Navy. The two captains—the line officer, Commander Moncy, who ran the ship and the senior medical officer, Captain Alanson Bryan—ate in lonesome splendor on the upper deck. The presidency of the officers' mess fell to the ship's executive officer, Lieutenant Commander J. B. Bliss, an old sea-dog who had long since lost all taint of his Minnesota origin. In his group were the other senior line officers, with appropriately Dickensian names, Lieutenants Parsons and Sly.

Several of the other older officers of the line were men from the merchant fleet reserve, quiet competent officers who seemed to feel not quite at home in the hierarchal atmosphere of the Navy. The junior line and engineering officers were almost all youngsters, so-called "ninety-day wonders" who had been plucked from the colleges and sent through hurry-up training schools by an expanding—one might almost say an exploding—Navy, in desperate need of trained man power. In the presence of these youngsters, I soon lost my feeling of being a landlubber. Most of them were on their maiden voyage, too, and quite as much at sea as I.

Against all these, the doctors stood apart. Even the few who were of the regular Navy made no pretense at being nautical characters. They were all primarily medical men. Most of them in fact had never been to sea before, for the *Relief* had spent the first year of the war as an auxiliary hospital in an East Coast harbor.

Typical of the best among them was Commander Donald J. McCarthy. Dr. McCarthy, who was in charge of all medical service on the ship, was a man of nearly fifty. He had entered the Navy as a young interne at the beginning of the last war, expecting sea duty, the usual lot of a young doctor. But instead he had spent *that* war at the Great Lakes Naval Training Station near Chicago. Despite his disappointment, the young doctor had become attached to the Navy. The attachment was not quite strong enough to make him stay on as a regular. But through all the years of building a practice in Minneapolis, of marrying and raising a family, of teaching at the University of Minnesota Medical School— through it all he retained the reserve commission.

Early in 1940, Dr. McCarthy was called to his second war. For a year, he examined recruits in his home town and did the other chores of a land-based naval doctor. For more than another year he served on the *Relief* on the east coast. Then, twenty-five years after he joined the Navy, McCarthy first went to sea, achieving war zone duty status only three months before his own son graduated from Annapolis. It was with a wry sort of humor that he wrote the boy, boasting, "It was a close shave, son, but I knew I could beat you to it."

McCarthy was the perfect picture of the intelligent, soft-spoken *wise* old doctor—*wise* in the finest meaning of that word. His months in the Navy had given him a chance to look back upon the busy years of medical practice and to think his way through to a philosophy of medicine, rounded and well formed. He knew the doctor's limitations, knew that many a cure was effected despite the physician rather than because of him. But he also knew how to win his way with a patient, how to make a sick and weary boy want to get well. He had that great essential of a great doctor, the ability to see people's miseries through their own eyes and never to lose sympathy with even the most trying of patients. More than anything else he typified to me the civilians in the Navy, the doctors who had not lost human touch despite their rank, their stripes and their uniforms.

✦

McCarthy's counterpart on the surgical side was Commander Edward Victor Denneen, a much younger man—tall, blue-eyed and good-looking. Ed Denneen too was a type; the movies would have cast him for a surgeon. He was a vigorous man, muscular and active despite the slight paunch which was beginning to develop around his middle. He played shuffleboard with dynamic energy, he played bridge as if life itself depended on the winning of each hand. In the operating room he also played for keeps, cutting sharply and decisively with never a second's hesitation. His drive to dominate any scene made him a difficult bridge partner. But one felt that inevitably it would make him a good surgeon. I know that if I were on the operating table, with the ether mask hovering above my face, there is no man I would rather see pulling on the gloves than forceful, self-confident —yes, egotistical—but definitely skillful Ed Denneen.

The other doctors ran the whole gamut of types. There was McCarthy's assistant, Lieutenant Commander Lyman Hoyt, an Iowa born Bostonian, whose many years of practice in that New England city had made him seem to partake more of Back Bay than even the Cabots—a man who seemed cold and reserved, who stood off alone. It was only after you knew Hoyt a long time that you discovered that the reserve covered a pleasing shyness, that beneath the seeming coldness was an immensely likable character, a precise and speedy brain and the sort of memory that always serves a physician in good stead.

There was Nick DeSanto, the clinical pathologist, a ruddy, black-haired, brown-eyed man with a weakness for piano practice. There were moments—when Nick stumbled over the same wrong note in the same piece for the fifteenth time —when you could have killed him and been acquitted by any jury chosen from the crew. But down in his laboratory, in the quiet of his room or basking on the penthouse deck, one found him an intensely friendly person, soft-spoken, mild-mannered, talkative in a quiet way.

There was Tom Garvey, the assistant in the surgical service, a doctor's son in a family of doctors. Tom supplied the humor for the ship, a dry sort of whimsical humor that came out of him in short puffs, even when he lay in pain as he did for most of the outward trip.

Tom's humor extended—as it seldom does with doctors—even to kidding that holy of holies, the sacredness of medicine. He had a persistent back injury—a sacro-iliac strain—which lingered despite all the ministrations of McCarthy, of Denneen, and of Commander Claiborne, who ran the x-ray work. But when we dropped a boat during an abandon ship drill and Tom Garvey tumbled thirty feet into Noumea harbor, he came up dripping, limping, but smiling still. And he insisted ever after that his back strain had been cured by the fall. "I always told you," he would tease Denneen, "those chiropractors have it all over us surgeons. You worked on me for months and here just one adjustment, one slap on the back with a boat-hook, and I am cured." Then while Denneen would grow choleric, Garvey would amble smilingly off, holding his limp in check until he had turned a corner and gone out of sight.

During all the long voyage to the Pacific, one did not see the doctors on the *Relief* under the best of circumstances. For any group of men, deprived of work, will rot and mildew a bit in the heat of the tropics. One felt the tendency affecting each of the doctors differently. But it did seem to affect all to greater or lesser degree—all, that is, except Charlie Hazzard.

Lieutenant Commander Hazzard was our urologist, more frequently referred to as "the plumber." A tall, heavy-set man with pink baby skin, half gray hair and a forehead like a cliff, Charlie seemed to be the only one of all those on board who realized that the prolonged, enforced vacation of our cruise was not doing anyone any good. He, at least, was the only one who did something decisive about it.

As we crossed the Equator and moved into the last long lap of our voyage, he began to send his corpsmen out "ambulance chasing" among the crew. A few days of their missionary work rounded up a dozen men who needed circumcision. And thus, when boredom and idleness had set most of the others to introspection or to bickering, Charlie Hazzard was busy in his operating room, keeping his hands in practice, training his corpsmen and relearning the skills lost in weeks of watching the sea go by.

It was a strange voyage we made, but not all our time was wasted. The ship itself was put in trim, converted from the messiness and disorder of the first days into a spit-and-polish model of a naval vessel. Our crew, most of them fresh out of boot camp, became the taut, traditional, happy crew of a vessel on active duty. Our corpsmen went to school, studied their procedures, took their examinations for re-rating.

After work was done the entire ship played as only Americans can. On several occasions we had boxing matches on the quarterdeck where a ring was erected over the great hatch. Here under cargo lights, with the crew arranged in tiers around the ring on the fo'c's'le, on the boats and in the rigging, with the officers and nurses in the balcony formed by the promenade deck, we witnessed that strange Navy institution with the sissified name of "happy hour."

I remember looking up towards the bridge one night while the excitement of the fights was at a high pitch. Ten men were assigned to the bridge. But in the reflected glare of the flood lights, I could see nine faces peering down at the fighters. Only the helmsman was on the job. I remember wondering what impression such a scene would have made on the Japanese had they boarded us at that moment. A strange, bewildering, decadent people they would no doubt have thought us, to act in such ways in the midst of a war.

It *was* strange. Yet there on the quarter-deck, one felt, was a large part of what these men were fighting for. Democracy was at work in that ring, expressing itself in curious ways. Many of the bouts were mixed fights between Negro mess attendants and white sailors. Most of the men who watched the fights had more than a spectator's interest in the outcome of the bouts; for even the Navy's rigid rules against gambling cannot prevent the placing of a private bet. Yet, though one knew these interests existed, though many of the boys were Southerners—with a Southerner's attitude toward the Negro deeply ingrained—despite all that, one never heard the slightest expression of prejudice. The cheers, the boos, and the cat-calls were all for the individual without regard to the color of his skin.

For nearly forty days we sailed, ambling our slow way across the Pacific without sighting a single ship.

Then one bright morning, the deep blue sea turned green and we saw the coral reefs and crenelated mountains of New Caledonia. Slowly we worked our way up the channels and around the bends into the beautiful harbor of Noumea. Around the last turn, we came past the stuttering signal blinkers on the hills and the great gray ships swinging everywhere at anchor. Then we dropped our own anchor at last, almost alongside another hospital ship, the heroine of Pearl Harbor, the *Solace*.

CHAPTER II

VETERAN IN WHITE SKIRTS

I HAD originally intended to proceed at the first opportunity to Guadalcanal and—if possible—beyond. Then, having seen the manner in which casualties were treated in the most advanced posts, I hoped to follow them through the intermediate hospitals, onto the hospital ships, to the rear bases and eventually back to the States.

Once in New Caledonia, however, I found that the *Solace* was about to leave, on a trip to New Zealand—a voyage which might be its last for months to come. This hospital ship, I knew, had carried most of the burden of evacuation in the South Pacific since it had appeared in those waters a short time after Pearl Harbor. Thus I temporarily abandoned my original schedules and sought passage on the *Solace*.

In the end the change of plans proved all for the best. For the view of naval medicine which I gained, on the *Solace* and in the hospitals in Auckland, served to dispel many of the illusions I had carried with me from the States. When, later, I went up the line, through the New Hebrides to Guadalcanal and Tulagi and the Russell Islands, I had a much better idea of what I wanted to see. I knew by then where the most interesting detachments were to be found, where to discover the specialists whose work represented major achievements in the war zone islands.

I learned too—I think—how to understand the men in the war zone and particularly the patients. For the men I met on the *Solace* and in New Zealand were already veterans. Like all old vets they were developing the narrative habit. They were glad to talk, glad indeed to fill any willing ear with the story of their experiences. In their talk one found a guide book to the habits, the peculiarities, the taboos and the crotchets of the men stationed in the tropic islands. Later, on many an occasion, this advance acquaintance with the kind of men I was to meet at our out-posts helped me to understand and to appreciate actions which, to the uninitiated, might have seemed bizarre and irrational.

Securing passage on the *Solace* was by no means an easy process. Commander C. L. Waters, captain of the *Solace,* was most cordial in inviting me to inspect and travel with his ship. But he was an extremely cautious man, determined to adhere not only to the spirit but to the letter of the Geneva Convention under which his ship—and all white hospital ships—operate.

Three times I went ashore and secured travel orders authorizing me to proceed on the *Solace*. Three times Captain Waters exercised his prerogative of rejecting these orders because, technically, their wording might possibly permit the enemy to allege that the *Solace* had been used as a transport.

At length I met the Captain in the personnel office in town and with his aid a final set of orders was drawn which stated the reasons for my accommodation on the *Solace*. The orders made clear that I was to be taken onto Commander Waters' ship "for the purpose of gathering material for a book on hospital ships as authorized by the Secretary of the Navy."

Only then, when certain that he had protected the immunity of his vessel, would Captain Waters accept me. By that time the *Solace's* departure was imminent. I rushed back to the *Relief*, packed my bags, cleared my papers, bid a hasty good-by to my friends and hurtled into a boat only to see the anchor of the *Solace* break water. The great white ship was just getting under way as the coxswain of the *Relief's* boat made frantic efforts to get me aboard. For a time we bobbed along in the wake of the slow-moving ship. At length we came within hailing distance and a deck officer called to us through a megaphone.

Between the noise of our motor and the splashing of the waters, it was impossible to make out his words. His gestures, a wild waving of the hands, could only mean—it seemed to us—"Turn back and go home." Reluctantly we swung aside and watched the great red crosses move away.

The coxswain who had bet his pride on getting me aboard the *Solace*, was even more dejected than I. He leaned way over on his tiller, so that he could see me under the canvas awning, and he poured out his apologies. He was still leaning there—still explaining—when the boat suddenly lurched. We both looked up to find another boat alongside—a boat with the letters S.O.L. painted on its prow.

Those letters had always had a different meaning for me. But now they provided *solace* indeed. In the roughening waters, while the sailors held the boats together with their hooks, my bags were heaved into Captain Waters' gig. Then I was heaved after them—wet, dishevelled, and out of breath. The *Relief's* coxswain waved a gay good-by and we turned about to follow the *Solace* out of the harbor.

Once the transfer had been achieved and the big white ship was looming closer again, I realized that a swarm of other boats had gathered about us. Now they formed a procession behind us and like baby dolphins we all tagged after the mother ship. As I climbed aboard the *Solace's* ladder I received a final send-off from this coxswain's quorum as each little boat rang its bells and shifted its gears as noisily as possible before they dispersed to re-assume their separate paths.

The *Solace* was a veteran. You felt it as soon as you came aboard. There was no fumbling on the quarter-deck, no hesitation as to what to do, even with a war correspondent. In less than ten minutes my orders had been taken from me and sent to the offices for entry in the log, my bag had been moved to a room in the sick officers' quarters and my somewhat dishevelled form had been guided to the wardroom where I met the *Solace's* officers as they gathered for dinner.

She was a happy ship too. One felt welcome not only because people went through the motions of making you welcome but also because everyone on board seemed to be a friend of everyone else. That first night, at supper, I was struck by the tremendous *esprit de corps* which I later found pervaded the entire ship. It isn't an easy thing to describe but there was nothing subtle about it when you saw it. For the men of the *Solace* were proud—proud as punch—of the job they had been doing for fourteen months.

They questioned me politely about the *Relief*. But one felt that they were certain, even before I replied, that the answers would simply confirm their feeling that the *Solace* was the best ship in the business. And one after another, through that first evening, the doctors and the other officers came over and offered to show me their part of the ship's work. The offers did not carry any of the taint of publicity seeking; these men did not care whether I wrote about the *Solace* or not. They simply took it for granted that their great ship— their wonderful, accomplished, historic ship—and every component part of it—would be of intense interest to me.

They were not far wrong. For the *Solace* was a great ship, the finest, most modern hospital vessel anywhere afloat. And she was manned by a group of medical officers whose record of accomplishment is one of the proudest in the Navy Medical Corps.

She was smaller than the *Relief* and in only this respect did she suffer by comparison, for in rough weather the *Solace* had a tendency to pitch her head into the sea, rearing again like a lively filly as she came out of the trough of a wave. Her hull was that of the old Cuba liner *Iroquois*. But in 1940 the Navy had ripped everything out of that hull with the exception of one great, winding staircase. In place of the staterooms and passageways of the old vessel, the Brooklyn Navy Yard had built the last word in hospital installations.

Down in her hold the *Solace* had speed, great turbines that pushed her through the water at half again the rate of the *Relief*. Because of that speed she was half again as much a ship as the *Relief* could possibly be. Her carrying capacity was almost equal to that of the *Relief*. But, with her speed, she could complete three trips in the time it took her older sister to make two. Such speed for a hospital ship had proved important in two ways. Not only did it increase the number of patients she could carry in a given period, it also increased each patient's chance of survival and safe delivery to a rearward port. For with each hour of her busy run the *Solace* pulled further from the war zone, further from the region where Jap submarines might lurk, and nearer to the base hospitals where cures are completed.

In her equipment the *Solace* had a twenty-year edge over the *Relief*. The mistakes that had been made in designing that first pre-planned hospital ship had been carefully annotated by the designers of the new vessel. Her wards—with one exception—were all above deck; great airy rooms ventilated by a powerful—and surprisingly noiseless—system of pumps. Her operating rooms and her specialized laboratories —x-ray, dental, physio-therapeutic, and so forth—were crammed with the latest types of shiny, chrome-plated equipment.

Commander H. P. Schenck, the senior ophthalmologist on the staff, took me through his clinic's quarters—largely, I think, for the pleasure of watching me gape and gasp as he unveiled each new gadget of a tremendous array. "When I first came aboard," he told me, "I used to think of all this stuff as a tremendous waste of the taxpayers' money. For whoever furnished these quarters must have ordered the entire catalogue of every supply house. But since then there have been many times, these last fourteen months, when I have blessed that supply officer. Because if you want a man to develop some rare malady, something that calls for the kind of instrument only one ophthalmologist in a thousand would possess, all you have to do is send that man into some Godforsaken corner of the earth like the Solomons. We have had cases here with trick conditions that I haven't seen in all my years back in Philadelphia. And when such cases come along, it is a wonderful feeling to know that you just have to reach out your arm to find every last imaginable gadget you could possibly want."

But you can't cure men with chromium. The record of the *Solace* is due without a doubt to the caliber of the physicians who sailed her. For the medical staff of the *Solace* was a unit of reserves drawn, as a body, from the Medical School and hospital of the University of Pennsylvania. The ship's senior medical officer, in accordance with Navy practice, was a regular, Captain Melville Joseph Aston. But under him were nearly a score of physicians and surgeons who in the past had worked together in civil life.

The unit had, in fact, been the first of a long series founded in peacetime by the Navy. Its driving spirit was Captain Richard Arminius Kern, for many years professor of clinical medicine at the Graduate School of Medicine of the University of Pennsylvania. Dr. Kern had started the unit in 1934, gradually gathering around him a number of his fellow professors, surgeons like L. Kraeer Ferguson, chief of the industrial clinic at the University of Pennsylvania hospital; J. T. Nicholson, professor of orthopedic surgery at the University of Pennsylvania Graduate School; and Commander Schenck, professor of ophthalmology. Around these men as a nucleus others had gathered, younger men like Robert S. Wigton who had studied at the University of Pennsylvania Institute of Neurology and later served as an instructor in neurology at the Women's Medical College of Pennsylvania and the University of Pennsylvania Medical School.

Captain Kern had served on the earlier *Solace*, a hospital ship which had won no little distinction in the first World War. He came with his unit to the new *Solace* shortly after Pearl Harbor, when the white-skirted lady received its baptism of fire. Thus, when I boarded the ship, its medical personnel was completing fifteen full months of active duty, most of it spent in the South Pacific. During that time the *Solace* had carried the vast majority of the battle casualties which arose from Guadalcanal and from the battles of the Coral Sea and of Santa Cruz.

Its doctors, men who had been medical and personal friends for many years, knew how to co-operate in their new field of endeavor. The older men respected the younger ones, for they had selected these protégés, trained them and watched them grow. And the younger men, far from looking upon their superior officers with a jealous eye, continued the attitudes of respect and admiration which they had first developed for these doctors when they studied under them in the quiet of the Philadelphia campus. Both groups, which differed only in age, were suffused by the feeling that they had met and licked the most difficult job which had ever faced them. *Esprit* literally oozed from them as they cited the ship's proud record or as they guided me through their wards to show me their more spectacular cases.

One felt the cohesion of the group especially when the men talked of a grievance which seemed to gnaw at all of them. Some months before, Bob Morse had come aboard their ship and photographed it from top to bottom for *Life*. They had liked Morse—as did everyone else in the Pacific— and had gone to great pains to let the effervescent little pho- tographer see everything and snap everything. Then Bob had carefully tagged his pictures, more than four hundred of them, and shipped them off to New York.

The doctors waited anxiously for the story to appear. When the issue finally arrived they crowded around it in the wardroom and greeted each crowded page of pictures with approval. But when they reached the last page of the story, their faces fell, for someone with an over-developed sense of the dramatic had selected a single one of Morse's pictures and blown it up as a full page smash finish to the article. That picture was a view of the wicker baskets in the ship's refrigerated morgue.

I could all the more appreciate the doctors' indignation at this distortion of their work when I learned something that *Life* had not printed, the amazing record of life-saving which these men had achieved. For, in its fifteen months of service, the *Solace* had carried nearly eight thousand casual- ties, the sick and wounded from all our bases in the South Pacific, from the battle of the Coral Sea, from Santa Cruz, from Guadalcanal and Tulagi. And of all those thousands, only eight had died!

My room in S.O.Q. (sick officers' quarters) was a double one, which I shared with Captain Edward P. Dupras. I was particularly interested in Dupras for he was the first casualty I had met, a twenty-three-year-old marine from Guadalcanal. His chart said that he was being evacuated because of a fractured wrist and a third or fourth relapse of malaria. But neither of these maladies troubled Dupras in the slightest. What bothered him was a disease which he called "Cactus Crut." It was my first contact with the strange new language which has sprung up in the South Pacific, a vivid, disrespectful, virile language which will yet confuse and astonish the poor parents of marines who will have to decipher it after the war.

The Captain's crut turned out to be a tropical fungus infection, a sort of ringworm which covered most of his body. It had been painted with a colorful purple solution—gentian violet perhaps—and every few hours the attending corpsman would sprinkle the Captain from head to foot with a white powder. This procedure was supposed to suppress the itching, but I gradually gathered that its principal function, as far as Dupras was concerned, was to give him something to do—an interlude in the boredom of having to be in bed. For Dupras was nothing if not energetic. He talked and sang and jumped out of bed and dressed himself and then undressed himself and got back into bed and combed his hair and mussed it up and did a thousand other things during the days I spent with him—things which negated each other and left him still scratching his crut.

That first night we both sat up in bed and talked, he pumping me about the way things were in the States and I trying to break through the language difficulty to learn something about Guadalcanal. It wasn't easy to understand him. In the end I took out my typewriter and he dictated the first few pages of what later became a fairly extensive dictionary of South Sea Island lingo.

The S.O.Q. corpsmen had told me that Dupras wore the Navy Cross. After we got to know each other I asked him about it. His first response was to pass it off with, "Oh, I just

happened to be around when the medals were handed out."
When I pressed him further he came up with a fanciful tale
of terrific exploits until he noticed my pencil had ceased writing. The third try he gave me the straight story of repelling
the Jap attack at Bloody Ridge.

As he told it, none of the men involved—himself least
of all—seemed to play a heroic part. They were simply men
who found themselves in a position where certain things
had to be done—and they did those things. That attitude—
which I later found so common among all the veterans of
Guadalcanal—pervaded all of Dupras's speech. He affected
an air of cynicism, professing a casual disrespect for the men
under him, his superior officers, the Navy as a whole and
the Army in particular. But behind it—and sticking through
his conversation in spite of himself—was the feeling that he
and a few thousand others were men of a special fraternity,
men set aside by their experiences on Guadalcanal, who would
always have more in common with each other than they
would with the rest of the world.

It was the old veterans' state of mind, in gestation. I have
seen it since in hundreds of men who enjoy—more than anything else—telling each other about the experiences they have
all been through. No doubt the psychiatrists have an explanation for the phenomenon. Perhaps it is some form of catharsis
which aids men in adjusting themselves to the rest of the
world by recalling and reliving their experiences in the days
when all the world seemed to have abandoned them.

At one point in our long conversations I asked Dupras
what the men on Guadalcanal thought of the psychoneurotic
breakdown cases, of the men who cracked up in battle.

"Look, buddy," he answered, his voice taking on an aggressive tone, "don't get the idea that anybody thinks they're
yellow. Hell, no! What you think when a guy cracks up is
that it was just lucky that it wasn't you. Those Japs are dirty

fighters—they like to fire a lot at night when all good people should be sleeping. And if you can't sleep and you're exposed and then some jerk from intelligence comes out of a plane and says you will be relieved ten days from now—only that was two weeks ago—then you crack up, that's all."

He leaned back and lit a cigarette and scratched a while. "You know," he said, "the only time I felt sorry for any of those Jap bastards was when we found one of the little monkeys crawling around on his hands and knees on the beach. He was crazy as a loon by then, so crazy he didn't even know who we were. He got the idea that we were an inspection party of his own officers and he kept bowing down low to us and talking a blue streak in Japanese. Then he heard us speak English and he went white under the yellow. He turned around and everywhere he turned he saw some more of us. I think that was when the last part of his brain gave way. Because he just let out one big yell and ran right into the ocean. Some of the boys wanted to take a shot at him but we held them back and the poor monkey just swam out as far as he could and then he either got a cramp—or a shark got him—or he just gave up. One moment we saw him bobbing around and the next there was just a hand in the air. And then he was gone.

"The point is, that guy didn't commit suicide. And he wasn't running away from us, either. He was just so cracked-up he didn't know what was happening. Sometimes, when the Japs cracked, they walked right into our lines just dragging their gun or carrying nothing at all. And so dazed they didn't even know they were among us.

"But maybe that is all bad medicine," he concluded. "Maybe I don't figure these crack-ups the way the doctors do. All I know is—anybody who says he wasn't near cracking up on Guadalcanal, is a Goddamned liar."

✦

On the first morning I went through the orthopedic wards with Lieutenant Commander Nicholson. We had a comparatively light load on this trip and the men were spaced out comfortably on the lower bunks with the upper racks folded back against their stanchions, giving the ward an air of great roominess. Most of the men were old cases who had already received their surgical treatment at hospitals in the Hebrides or in New Caledonia. Now they lay in their great plaster casts, looking forward to a final spell in a hospital at Auckland and the speedy return to usefulness of their limbs.

The majority were men with fractured legs, for such fractures were one of the most frequent results of the fighting in the Solomons. In sharp contrast with the last war—where trench fighting and the use of mortars made head, necks, and chest wounds the most frequent of all—the fighting in the Solomons, with its emphasis on the sniper and the use of the machine gun or automatic rifle, seemed to concentrate injuries upon the lower part of the body. Fortunately, our techniques for handling fractures have made tremendous advances within the last generation. Had these been the soldiers of 1918 a good proportion of them would never have survived evacuation to a rear hospital. Most of the rest would have come in with badly infected open wounds and the doctors would have been confronted far more with the problem of treating these infections than with questions of orthopedic surgery.

As it was, almost all of Nicholson's cases were encased in heavy plaster casts which immobilized their limbs and closed their wounds against infection. The cast-immobilization technique, developed first by the American surgeon H. Winnett Orr, and rediscovered during the Spanish Civil War, is now almost universally used by the armed forces of all the fighting nations. A wounded man who has sustained a fracture is usually flown to a rear line hospital at the earliest opportunity. Many of the men I saw on the *Solace* had reached such hospitals on the afternoon of the day in which they were injured. Once in the rear they are taken immediately to surgery, where their wounds are cleaned and débrided. The bones are set in place and raw surfaces are dusted, either with sulfanilamide or microcrystalline sulfathiazole. Then large plaster casts are gently built up around the injured member and the doctor can thereafter—almost invariably—devote his attention principally to improving the patient's general condition.

For such men, Nicholson provided principally a greeting and a speedy examination—just enough to make sure that no untoward complication had developed since their transfer to the ship. Four or five of the men, however, were Nicholson's own cases—men who had been injured in or around New Caledonia and brought directly to the *Solace*. These fresher fractures received an infinitely painstaking examination. Their charts were checked in every detail. The doctor seemed particularly anxious to discover, through minute questioning of the men themselves, whether the casts were causing any pain or friction. In one instance alone did this questioning produce any positive result. That man was immediately scheduled for a more thorough examination and a rebuilding of his cast.

In the so-called "quiet room" at the end of the ward we examined other patients still further advanced towards full recovery. These were men whose fracture casts had been removed shortly before we sailed. Now they were ready to learn to re-use their limbs, to retrain and recondition muscles which had begun to atrophy under long weeks of immobilization. This retraining did not have to await their arrival in New Zealand. It started right on the *Solace*. Together with the physiotherapist, a chief petty officer, Nicholson examined each of a dozen men, encouraging them to flex their injured hands, or legs, or arms and thus determining both the progress which had been achieved so far and the course of treatment to be followed in the next few days.

I followed some of these men to the physiotherapy rooms. Those with injured legs were carefully helped into large monel metal tubs. Here they sat on boards, placed at the end of the tub, with their feet suspended in the warm water. Then, while they read a book or "shot the breeze" with their neighbors, a mechanical agitator worked warm currents of water around the injured muscles. I was invited to try the treatment. It provided a soft tingling sensation much like the touch of a well-trained masseur. Smaller baths were used for injured arms and hands. In such baths the men were trained to try finger flexes while the hands were under water.

At the other side of the room were sun-ray lamps and massage tables. One man, a burned flyer now almost fully recovered, was lying under a sun-lamp carefully tanning the new skin, which covered his burns, in the hope of achieving a match with the dark tan of the rest of his body. "I've got a date with a babe in Auckland," he explained.

"Keep your shirt on, buddy," answered the physiotherapist. "I've got a date with a dozen."

As is always the case among doctors, they talked most easily about their unusual or bizarre patients—the least typical of the lot. Several of these had become almost legends on the *Solace*—some humorous, some tragic.

There was, for instance, the man who received a .25-caliber Jap bullet through the thigh. The doctors at the dressing station could see the wound of entry but there was no corresponding exit wound. Yet the bullet was nowhere to be found. He was brought aboard the *Solace* five days after his injury and the surgeons rushed him to an x-ray table. Sure enough, they found the bullet lodged neatly in his bladder.

The doctors scratched their heads and went into consultation, trying to determine just how to proceed toward the removal of the Jap slug. It seems that there are several procedures which may be used. Each has its complications and, hence, each has its violent proponents and opponents. The debate might have gone on indefinitely had not Mother Nature stepped in. While the doctors argued, a corpsman arrived bearing a pellet of lead in his hand. "Say, doc," he questioned, "what shall we do about Sergeant Bashwitz? He just passed this in his urine."

The sergeant, who is probably still called "Machine-Gun Joe," left the ship wearing the bullet on a string around his neck.

Another case "for the record" was that of a sailor injured in the battle of Savo Island. This patient was at his gun until a large enemy shell put it out of commission. At that time, the gunner recalled, something hit him on his chest. He looked down and realized that the blow had been struck by a part of his own lower jaw. Fearing that he might bleed to death the young sailor took his under-shirt and tied it to form a bandage securing the jaw in place.

At the time the ship was being abandoned. But he had no desire to leave. Instead he went below and released several trapped men. Then with their aid—and they later testified to this—he put out a fire in the sick bay. His only complaint was that, below decks, there was a haze of fine dust particles flying about, probably due to the flaking of paint from the ship's bulkheads. This haze caused him "some discomfort," so he finally emerged to the fo'c's'le.

His next recollection was of hitting the water. He could not recall going over the side. Apparently an explosion had blown him from the deck. In the water, he saw what he thought to be one of his buddies, clinging to a can. He swam over only to find a Jap who promptly tried to push him under. He swam around behind the Jap and managed to overcome him. Here again the otherwise incredible story was supported by the evidence of other casualties who recalled the incident.

After that, for two-and-a-half hours, he kept afloat using the can to support himself. When he was rescued he had been in the water for nearly three hours and it was nearly five hours after his injury before he received first aid.

The doctors, men not easily astonished, were almost unbelieving when they noted the rapidity of this patient's healing. Six weeks after his injury, the fracture of his mandible had knitted completely and the torn flesh had grown neatly back into place. He talked well, ate his food without difficulty and—while on the *Solace*—looked forward to the plastic operation which would restore a normal appearance to the jaw which had already regained its normal usefulness.

This was the first of many instances I came across in which immersion in salt water after injury seemed to benefit the casualty. The *Solace's* doctors had many theories to explain the phenomenon. Some ascribed it to the astringent action of the water, which limited bleeding and thus prevented the onset of shock. Others felt that shock was inhibited by the salt water simply because it limited the loss of skin moisture. Those who subscribed to this theory noted that a relatively small loss of skin moisture—caused by an extensive burn— brings on a large drain of the fluid content of the blood. In many a burn case arising from naval action, men who were thrown into the water were found to be in much better condition than those who remained exposed to the air. Frequently such men were quite unaware of the extent of their burns until sometime after their resue.

A third theory ascribes the beneficial action of a sea immersion to the manner in which salt water seems to inhibit the development of an infection. Many a case brought out of the water after as long as eight hours of immersion subsequently recovers without the development of infection. Men with similar injuries on land—who are forced to wait an equally long period before treatment—are very frequently found to suffer from severe infections.

The *Solace* had had several cases of men who were attacked by sharks, but who survived to tell the tale. One of the most dramatic of these was a patient whom I later met in New Zealand, a naval lieutenant whose ship was shot from under him on the night of October 12, 1942. For twelve hours he was in the water, swimming around in the dark amidst the wreckage and debris. At daybreak he found himself alone on the sea—alone except for a shark about five feet long which circled about him some twenty feet away.

The lieutenant, tired and dazed by his long struggle in the water, felt for the knife which all men carry when fighting in the tropics. But it wasn't there. So he faced the shark, treading water and turning slowly while the fish revolved around him. Every ten minutes or so the blood-maddened creature stopped his circling, poised on his tail for a second and then lunged at the wounded man. Each time the lieutenant attempted what he called "evasive action." Most of the time he succeeded and the shark went whizzing by to resume its circling. But often enough the attack struck home and the lieutenant felt the sharp teeth cutting at his arms or legs.

After a time he discovered that he could beat the shark off by hitting it on its sensitive snout. And so until eleven the next morning, when a rescue ship arrived, the young lieutenant and the shark boxed there in the water. When they finally rescued him he was literally cut to ribbons. Even the

cold words of the record of his physical examination bespeak
the horror which the man must have gone through. They
read,

Left forearm lacerated. Wound at elbow, one by three inches.
Left hand, dorsal surface, several small lacerations. Right foot,
numerous lacerated wounds over dorsum of toes and ankle. Left
thigh, lacerated. Wound, five inches long, transversely across
lower lateral thigh. Left foot and ankle, lacerated wounds over
both malleolus and heel. Numerous lacerations of great toe.

Yet this man too, survived and grew well. Fortunately the
shark did not get to any of the great tendons. When he was
rescued, twelve full hours after the disaster to his ship, he
fell into shock. But blood plasma soon relieved that and
sulfanilamide crystals in his wounds brought about a rapid
and uneventful recovery. Once again the medics marveled
at the amazing preservative powers of an enforced saline
bath.

The doctors of the *Solace* unit were unusually well situated to observe and compare the medical practices of all the
hospitals and dispensaries and ship sick bays operating north
of New Caledonia. While I was on their ship they had already started an extensive analysis of such cases—a project
which has since served to clear up a number of unsettled
questions and to guide many a physician or surgeon in an iso-
lated post.

Bob Wigton, the ship's young neurologist, took me
through the charts and outlines of an article on burns which
he was preparing—together with others—for eventual publi-
cation in the *United States Naval Medical Bulletin*. From
May, 1942 to April, 1943, their ship had handled more than
three hundred and fifty burn casualties. Fifty-six burn cases
had been received from the aircraft carrier *Wasp*, six days

after that ship was lost. Fifty more had been brought in from the *Quincy*, again after six days in transit. Fifty-six of the crew of the *Hornet* and its accompanying vessels reached the *Solace* on the fourth day after injury. A number also came from the *Atlanta* and its accompanying vessels. And many men, who suffered their injuries in the screaming solitude of a falling plane or in one of the so-called "industrial accidents" which occur periodically on ships and on shore, also swelled the *Solace's* rosters.

Coming from so many diverse sources, passing through so many different hands, the treatments which had been accorded to these men ran the whole gamut of burn therapy. And that gamut is broad, for much of what we have learned about burns is the result of very recent researches. There are a dozen ways of treating a burn, each with its proponents, each with its own specialized technique. Every method has its own advantages. But obviously the specialized conditions of naval warfare in the tropics must throw the weight in favor of one or two methods as against most of the others. It was to the task of discovering just where the preponderance of favorable features lay that Wigton and the others were devoting themselves.

In making their analysis they discovered several new points about burn treatment, and rediscovered many others. They found that the much touted paraffin-wax spray—which in 1942 was the latest fad in burn treatment—produced results which were almost uniformly unfavorable. They confirmed the growing opinion of many surgeons as to the limitations of the once universally used tannic acid treatment, and they proved to their own satisfaction—and that of most other naval surgeons—that sulfathiazole ointments—preferably prepared with the microcrystalline form of sulfathiazole—are perhaps the best treatment we have yet developed for burns, at least for use under the limiting conditions of naval warfare. In one of the cases which came before the doctors of the *Solace*, the patient had lost fully 80 per cent of his body surface. Such a case by any previous standards of treatment would almost certainly have died. Yet sulfathiazole ointment, blood plasma, and prompt treatment combined to pull the man through.

The analytical work carried on by Kern and others on his staff (and by the doctors of many a rearward hospital as well) is filling a crying need; one which came particularly to my attention when I reached the more advanced posts. For in the beginning, doctors "up the line" had little means of learning what happened to their patients after they shipped them on. The reserve doctors—former civilians—felt this lack most strongly for they were used to working in large city hospitals where almost every case could be followed through to its eventual recovery. They wanted desperately to know how their cases were making out and whether the treatments they were using were the best they could devise.

As I worked my way northward, later on, I found myself being converted into a sort of amateur medical missionary. At each new station I was submitted to a barrage of questions which I had to answer—as best I might—before I could turn the tables and begin to interview the doctors. On several occasions, I was asked to address the entire staffs of some hospital, to fill—in my amateur way—the gap in their knowledge which they all felt so acutely.

As a layman, I felt myself inadequate for the task. Often I was stymied by highly technical questions. Yet even the little I had to contribute—simply because I had seen the rearward hospitals and these men hadn't—seemed to be highly appreciated.

All that, of course, is in the past. Today, such work is much more highly organized. Definitive reports, analyzing hundreds upon hundreds of cases, are now appearing both in the *Naval Medical Bulletin* and in the air-mailed BU-MED photostatic letters, which the Navy Bureau of Medicine and Surgery circulates to every one of its far-flung outposts. The individual doctor may still not always learn precisely what happens to *his* individual cases. But through the work of doctors such as the *Solace* group, he can quickly learn the over-all results of various methods of treatment. And thus he may rapidly adjust his own methods to conform with what experience has proved to be the best practice.

The *Solace's* speed ended our journey all too soon . . . for me if not for the patients. On the third afternoon we sighted the raw, bare headlands of northern New Zealand and began our run down the coast to Auckland. In the lee of that coast the winds abated and every patient who could dress himself moved out of the wards and onto the decks. There they leaned on the rails smoking and joking and trying to hide from each other their joy at seeing civilized land and their anticipation of the pleasures of life in a climate free from tropical heat, rain, mosquitoes, and malaria. And yet, try as they would, they could not hide that excitement. It bubbled out of them and showed itself in every comment— in the way they packed their barracks bags eight and ten hours before there was any hope of our landing—in the way they searched the bleak coast for houses or boats or trails or even the smoke of a fire that would signify some human occupancy. Long before supper time the line of men who waited at the mess hall extended far down the passageways as if getting through with their meal early would somehow speed them on their course.

By nightfall we were well down the coast, and by nine o'clock we passed our last turn and headed into Auckland harbor. The sky had long since clouded over and a gentle rain had begun to fall, a rain which chilled all of us who stood on deck in our light tropical clothes. The first sensation on reaching New Zealand was this surprise—which seemed to hit everyone at once—that we were out of the tropics at last and back in a land where nightfall meant coolness. We stood on the rain-drenched decks—the cripples, the sick, the malarial—and literally gloried in the chilliness.

Throughout the ship the patients waited. Time and again I saw a man forced to reopen his too early packed bag to get out some object, a comb, a pipe, or a handkerchief. By supper time, half the doctors and most of the officers had donned their blues in place of the khakis which are the standard tropical uniform. When the order came for baggage to be piled on the quarter-deck gangways, the tension which had mounted all afternoon seemed to reach a breaking point. One half expected that some of the more anxious men would jump to the dock even before our hawsers were tied to and the gangplanks lowered.

Then as we swung into the harbor, the mood changed. The blacked-out city, whose hills we could see through the rain, looked bleak and cold and somber. Something happened to the tugs that were to warp us into the pier and we stood offshore for an extra half hour before—at long last—we began to slip ever so slowly toward the dock, our ship pivoting on its bow and bringing its flank against the wide dock wall. Along the wide dock, a row of ambulances could be seen winding in slowly from the shoreside and passing through a gate that led them to the far side of the dock to reappear again around the seaward end from which they proceeded along the stringpiece in a long line, their headlights all pointing shoreward.

In the unexpected coolness and strange quiet that one feels only over water, the scene on the slowly approaching dock made an impression of infinite sadness—the sadness of pure routine. The homecoming heroes were to be greeted, it seemed, only to be carted away with hardly a distinction to be made between the men and the baggage below.

And then, the unexpected happened. From the shore a band emerged, a raucous, off-tune band, its men marching in a ragged line but with plenty of vigor and an um-pah horn that sent its bellows clear across the harbor. It didn't play the "Star Spangled Banner," or "God Save the King," or any other song you might have expected. It played instead the "Boolah, Boolah" song of Yale.

Yet no notes were ever more welcome to men's ears. The entire ship's company and all the patients lined the rail and the noisy band literally drew us up to the dock. The corpsmen came on deck bringing the stretcher patients who craned their necks to see over the high railing or leaned over the edges of the stretchers to catch a view of the scene through hawser holes and scuppers. Somehow it seemed as if on that dreary, rainy night all of New Zealand had turned out to welcome us. As we tied up at the pier, the great arc lights were switched on and the ambulance drivers started to warm up their motors. Corpsmen from the hospital ran up and down the dock trying to find their friends in the crew. At first only people who knew each other called out in greeting, but like a contagion the feeling spread and soon everyone on the dock below was talking to everyone on the decks above saying all sorts of things of little meaning which somehow added up to a welcome.

A gangway was jockeyed up against the ship and the patients began to go off. The stretcher cases came first and the hollow metallic clang of the ambulance doors as they closed on each departing group had a cheery note. The long line of khaki ambulances began to move away from the dock and was replaced by a string of busses into which the ambulatory patients crowded, singing now. Soon they too were gone and the band climbed aboard its bus. The music faded slowly into the distance, leaving only the sound of the winches as they began to pull from the dock the supplies needed for the ship's quick turn around next morning.

CHAPTER III

AUCKLAND

MY first view of Auckland that night was a confused one. I sat next to Captain Dupras in the sick officers' bus that drove us through the dim, misty city to the Mobile Base Hospital on the outskirts of town. For a time there was a depressed silence among the men as we stared out of the windows at the foggy streets. Dupras sat quietly, like the rest, scratching his crut, until we rounded a turn into Queen Street and the young marine caught sight of a skirt.

"Hey, fellers," he cried. "Lookit. Women! Real live women. Oh boy, oh boy, oh boy, oh boy, oh boy . . ."

The rest of the men turned around, startled at first and then smiling, condescending and amused. Frenchy, the reserve ensign who had sold his tuna schooner to the Navy and then sailed it himself across the Pacific, leaned over and tapped me on the shoulder. His thumb pointed at Dupras and he said, "Helluva lot of use he'll have for women—with that crut of his."

But Dupras was not the least bit abashed. It was fun to see girls again, even if only through the window of a bus. So every time another skirt hove into sight our battered vehicle echoed with "Oh boy—women—real, live women."

He was still chattering about them twenty minutes later, when we rounded the last turn and passed the sentries at the hospital gates. We drew up at the administration building and a lantern-jawed nurse heaved herself into the bus.

"O.K., gentlemen," she said in a foghorn voice. "End of the line."

We all filed out of the bus, the marine coming last. He dropped his barracks bag from his shoulder and sat down on it. He rolled a butt, lit it and flipped the match away. Then he took another look at the old battle-ax who was just stepping out from the bus.

"Jeez!" he said. "Jeez! Real nurses, too."

When we left the dock the last of the enlisted men's long parade of ambulances and busses had just rolled out of sight ahead. By the time we reached the hospital every last man, of the 183 we had brought with us, was in a bed, identified and classified and eating a hot supper before going to sleep. In nearly a year of working together, the men of the *Solace* and of the Auckland hospital had routinized the transfer of patients so that not a minute was wasted. Before leaving the ship each casualty was tagged with a card which not only identified him, by name, number, and diagnosis, but also indicated exactly which ward and which bed in the hospital was allotted to him. When the busses and ambulances drew into the hospital compound they had only to circle the roads that ran to the wards to discharge each patient at the proper point. Long before they arrived, the doctors and nurses in the various wards received the medical records of the patients who were coming. These records, arranged and classified on the ship, were dropped to the dock even before the gangplank was lowered. A motorcycle courier rushed them to the hospital. By the next morning every incoming patient was fully integrated into the hospital's routine.

The Auckland Naval Hospital was designated as a Mobile Base. Actually, it was about as mobile as the First National Bank. For, as part of the lend-lease-in-reverse policy, the

New Zealand authorities had provided half the hospital's buildings and much of the labor that went into its erection. And the New Zealanders built well and solidly.

The hospital site was a high, level, sixteen-acre tract, a former cricket field. The Navy moved in late in July of 1942 and the flat, open moor soon blossomed with a rash of prefabricated steel buildings. As usual, the doctors and the corpsmen turned engineers for the occasion, digging pits and pouring concrete footings, erecting the steel frames, sheathing the walls and installing electric wiring, plumbing, and other equipment.

Almost immediately, however, they found themselves aided by volunteer groups of New Zealanders. School boys turned up after their classes and quietly picked up shovels and set to work. Businessmen and workers spent their weekends helping with the construction. The cricket players, though driven off their field, appeared at their old haunt in overalls to add their labor to the general pool.

In twenty-eight working days forty-one complex prefabricated steel buildings were erected, furnished, and equipped. These included a power house with steel boilers, auxiliary electric generators, storerooms, galleys, laboratories, and x-ray and administration buildings. By August 20, the first group of 366 patients was received from the Solomons. And by that date the hospital had 380 beds ready for use.

Thereafter, for over a year, the hospital grew—although always just barely fast enough to accommodate the swelling stream of casualties. Immediately after the first consignment of wounded arrived, work was started on sixteen new wards, on additional barracks, a brig, storerooms, larger mess halls, a new administration building, and a neuropsychiatric ward. These buildings were supplied by New Zealand; sturdy structures of wood and cementboard with wide casement windows and steam heat.

By December of 1942, the hospital's capacity had more than trebled and stood at 1160 beds. In the next month a receiving barracks in a downtown park was taken over for use as a convalescent hospital, providing an additional thousand beds. The New Zealanders also made available the facilities of the Ellerslie Hospital and of the Auckland City Hospital.

During all this time the naval hospital was serving not only Navy and Marine personnel but that of the Army as well. Until the Army completed its own hospital in the area, fourteen Army medical officers and several hundred Army corpsmen and nurses co-operated in running the mixed unit. The naval staff consisted of nearly sixty doctors and many hundreds of corpsmen, technicians, and nurses.

Meanwhile, the *Solace* and other vessels were bringing in patients, literally "by the boat load." The vast majority were Americans. But included in the more than eight thousand cases which the hospital handled in its first eight months were the survivors of *H.M.S. Canberra*, the Australian cruiser that went down with our own ships in the battle of Savo Island, and of many another Australian or New Zealand unit or ship which fought beside our own men. Of the entire group of patients—men injured by shrapnel splinters, machine guns, bombs, and flash burns as well as thousands who suffered from malaria or other tropical diseases—only five died in those first months. Nearly half of the men were returned to active duty; a fourth more were transferred to other hospitals or remained on the patient rolls. The remaining quarter were shipped back for further hospitalization in the States.

One found no difficulty in understanding this amazing record after touring the hospital. For, except that its buildings were but one story high, it resembled in every respect a great hospital in the States. Its wards were large and roomy; cool and well ventilated in the warm Auckland summer,

heated and windproof in the chilly rainy winter season which
began in late April. The patients slept on beds furnished by
the New Zealanders, beds with wooden-slat springs which
turned out to be far softer and more comfortable than they
looked. Laboratories, service kitchens, operating rooms, and
other hospital facilities were of the highest standard—so high
in fact that New Zealand doctors, who came to visit and
compare, admitted that their own fine hospitals boasted nothing better. And the hospital staff was of a caliber to match
the excellence of its equipment; they were drawn largely
from the famous Crile Clinic of Cleveland, the clinic founded
and developed by that great surgeon of the first World War,
George Washington Crile.

The New Zealanders have gotten on well with our service
forces quartered on their islands. In the beginning, when it
seemed that the Japanese would sweep down and engulf
them, our small detachments were welcomed with flowers at
the docks and greeted as saviors. Later, when the novelty
had worn off, they found that they still liked our men,
enjoyed their ways, and appreciated their correct behavior
and good manners. Our soldiers and sailors in turn discovered that they had much in common with the New Zealanders. Their beer was tasty and potent. Their girls were comely
and friendly. They had no night clubs but they more than
made up for this lack by inviting our men into their homes.
Within the first year of our participation in the war, scores
of our service personnel posted a three hundred dollar passage money guarantee and secured their officers' permission
to marry New Zealand girls.

The hospital was a focus for these friendly relationships.
In the lines at the "Ship's Store" you would see many a
New Zealand soldier standing among our marines and
sailors to buy our low-priced, tax-free cigarettes. In the

wards, New Zealand Red Cross workers entertained the men with songs and accents which soon ceased to be quaint and trying to our ears. Ambulatory patients were allowed to leave the hospital on pass and they soon found a welcome in many an Auckland home.

The Auckland doctors early established cordial and friendly relations with our own medical men. They were invited to attend conferences at the hospital. And they, in turn, made our men the honored guests of their local medical meetings. Somehow at Auckland it seemed that all the mistakes that could have been made by a visiting armed force were avoided. The New Zealanders were more than mere formal allies. They practiced alliance and brought it to a fine art.

I was given a room in one of the surgeons' barracks and thus I found myself in constant contact with the doctors. Days were spent going through their wards and operating rooms. Evenings, they sat around—as doctors will—discussing their cases. At Auckland, I first ran into the feeling which seems to exist among all doctors in the South Pacific: the belief that all the other pastures are far greener than one's own. Doctors I met later, up-the-line in the war zone, yearned to be in Auckland with its city life, its temperate climate and all its other advantages. But most of all they yearned to be at the Auckland Naval Hospital where—as they fondly imagined it—"one could really practice medicine."

But doctors at Auckland had a different dream. They described their work as the "tail-endings"; watching most men recover because of the good work of the first doctors who saw them; helping a few to recover despite the shortcomings —the only occasional shortcomings—of harried surgeons up-the-line. They longed to get into the Hebrides and the Solomons or on to the cruisers and battleships. They wanted action and excitement. But most of all they had an idea that you practiced "real medicine and real surgery" when you were near the battle fronts.

Fortunately, for the peace of mind of both groups, it seems to be the Navy's policy to rotate most of its medical men, alternating a tour of duty at the front with a spell at a rear line hospital. Many a doctor, whom I met in Auckland pining for the tropics, later got his wish. Many of them are no doubt pining today, with equal fervor, for the beautiful hospital in New Zealand.

In the beginning the vast majority of the hospitals' cases fell to the surgeons, Lieutenant Commanders R. J. Kennedy, Joe Roberts and Max John Knight, and Lieutenants George Crile, Jr., and Hays Richman Yandell. Most of these men were Crile Clinic doctors (young Crile is the son of the Clinic's founder and, like his father, a born surgeon) long used to working as a team. Their patients came to them already well on the way toward recovery. But often their skill made all the difference between a partial, limited, crippling recovery and full rehabilitation.

Occasionally a case came through which developed surprising complications. One such was that of a sailor who had been hit by a shell fragment on board his ship. He had received first-aid treatment and his wound had been packed with sulfanilamide. When he arrived at the hospital the great gaps along his thigh—one of them eight inches in length and two in width—were healing neatly with clean, granulating tissue growing rapidly into place. For a time this seemed to be an ordinary case. The wounds continued to granulate cleanly. The patient had neither pain nor other complaints. The doctors were about ready to go ahead with a skin graft, but they were disturbed by a small draining sinus in the center of the largest wound.

Just as a precaution, they took an x-ray, only to find a

great jagged, boomerang-shaped shell fragment imbedded deep in the flesh near the hip joint. It had gone unnoticed on the man's ship, where x-ray equipment was not available. Because it caused no pain it had gone unnoticed ever since.

Probing deeply through the open wound the doctors could feel the foreign body. Finally they managed to grasp its tip with a surgical clamp. Then, without anaesthesia and without discomfort to the patient, they gave one tug and the shell fragment came out through the wound. The ugly piece of metal was over an inch wide and more than five inches long. Once it was removed, the wound healed promptly and the patient was soon back on his feet.

The doctors were careful to point out that the presence of a foreign body in a wound at Auckland is no evidence of poor surgery up-the-line. In many cases it has been desirable —at the point of primary operation—to leave small foreign bodies in the wound, for later excision. Sometimes surgeons will even find it preferable to leave a shell fragment permanently in place. Even when, as is usually the case, removal seems desirable, it is often preferable to wait until shock has passed and the patient has recovered his strength before attempting to disturb the already torn and lacerated flesh. This is particularly true of shell fragments and bomb fragment wounds incurred on ship board. For these pieces are red hot when they pierce the flesh. They sterilize their own pathways and thus there is little danger of their carrying infection into the wound. Wounds incurred in land fighting, on the other hand, often involve the presence of shreds of soiled clothing and of ground filth. The danger of infection is then much greater. Foreign bodies, in such cases, are usually excised at the first opportunity.

Lieutenant Yandell supervised the hospital's burn service. He was a young Oklahoman, a graduate of the Harvard University Medical School, tall, smooth-cheeked—a very serious and intense young man. He had an extremely gentle touch with his patients. I have watched him work for half an hour or more to remove a bandage from a sticky wound and in all that time his patient never once winced.

Like all burn wards, the one at Auckland was a depressing place. Even the less severe burns are ugly wounds showing great areas of raw, bloody flesh. The secondary effects of a burn—shock, dehydration, liver damage, etc.—often include the development of a pronounced depression in the patient. Despite all the doctors can do—and they can do a great deal nowadays—an extensive burn is an injury which causes great and prolonged pain, often aggravated by the slightest movement.

In Yandell's ward, however, the depressing quiet was modified by the hopeful outlook of the men. Those new to the ward looked forward with much apprehension to the grafting operations which would hasten their recovery. But, while the "beds" for their grafts healed, they had a chance to compare wounds with the veterans of the ward, those who had already received grafts. Usually, by the time their own turn came, the results they saw on their fellow patients not only reconciled them to the operation but made them anxious for it. Even during my short stay, several of the men pressed Dr. Yandell, asking, "When is my turn, Doc?"

In performing his grafts Yandell used a Padgett Dermatome, that incredibly accurate instrument which permits the surgeon to slice a layer of skin off the thigh, back or abdomen with absolute uniformity of thickness. Setting his instrument so as to cut a graft sufficiently thick to provide healthy coverage for the wound, Dr. Yandell was still able—with the dermatome—to leave sufficient skin on the donor area so that natural regeneration was quickly accomplished. Two of his cases had received their grafts some ten days before I arrived. In both instances the scar at the donor site, which measured four by eight inches, had almost disappeared. The receiving sites were covered with clear, smooth, healthy skin which already adhered firmly and naturally to the underlying flesh.

Like the doctors of the *Solace*, those at Auckland avoided grafts wherever possible, preferring to let the skin regenerate itself from the tiny fragments left around hair roots and from the edges of the wound. But, on many a severe burn, this process would take far too long and would leave the wound exposed to potential infection. On such wounds skin grafts hastened recovery and produced amazingly fine results.

As the months went by at Auckland the balance between surgical and medical cases shifted. The first casualties from the Solomons were almost entirely surgical, for the men had not been long enough on Guadalcanal and Tulagi to be infected by malaria or other tropical diseases. Later, shipments of men from the northern islands included large groups of malaria victims—in one instance 80 per cent of all those arriving on a hospital vessel. Frequently men who were brought in with wounds or suffering from any of a great variety of diseases, were later found to also carry malaria.

After the turn of the year, when malaria control work really got under way in the Solomons, the balance shifted once again, although Auckland continued to receive many malaria cases, particularly those of men who had suffered several relapses. Many of these men, after a clinical course of treatment at Auckland, were not immediately returned to duty in the tropics but were either retained in New Zealand or sent back to the States. Everyone felt that a man who had had two—or three, or four—relapses had suffered enough and was due for a tour of duty in a safely non-malarious zone.*

✦

* Much of the most interesting work I saw in the South Pacific, both in the treatment of malaria and in psychiatry, has been carried on in

Leaving Auckland, I took a short vacation from naval medicine, traveling on a supply ship. In Noumea, I rejoined the *Relief*. But it was no longer the ship I had left—the inexperienced vessel with an inexperienced crew. For in the weeks of my absence, the *Relief* had been receiving many casualties and the doctors, who had so little to do on our outward journey, had been busy indeed.

A day or two after my return, they got their first breathing spell when we trans-shipped our patients to other vessels and to the hospitals ashore. They were an excited, happy group when we finally raised anchor and started up-the-line for Espiritu Santo. Their first taste of real war medicine in the tropics had taught them many of their shortcomings and made them aware of how much they did not know. But it had also taught them that they, too—like the doctors of the *Solace*—were a good team when they had work to do. This time, when the ship was emptied and the voyage began again, the doctors did not sit around and bicker, as they had during the last weeks of our long trip from the States. Instead they met in daily medical conferences, exchanging experiences and preparing themselves for the still heavier duty they could expect in the northern New Hebrides.

As I toured the ship again and was greeted by my old friends among the doctors, the nurses, and the corpsmen, I could feel the story of the *Solace* beginning all over again. For now the *Relief* was a "blooded" ship, beginning to develop its own *esprit de corps*.

Auckland. It has seemed to me, however, that I could give a clearer picture of both these fields of medicine by treating them in separate chapters. The reader will find malaria discussed in Chapter VIII, and the treatment of the psychiatric casualties in Chapter XII.

CHAPTER IV

HOSPITAL IN A SWAMP

ALL through the spring and early summer of 1942—while the Japs were liquidating Bataan and driving the British out of Malaya and the Dutch out of Sumatra and Java—American forces were engaged in a desperate, if less spectacular, struggle to keep open the life-line to Australia. As the Japanese flood flowed onward to New Guinea, to New Britain, and then down the Solomon chain, it seemed as if nothing could stop it. For all that we held, with any degree of security, were a few small fortified posts—one could hardly have called them bases—in Samoa, the Fijis, Tonga-Tabu, and New Caledonia. And yet, the Navy managed to check the Japs in a series of daring sea and air encounters and to pin them down at the southern end of the Solomons chain.

Meanwhile, with what forces were available we began to move northward through the islands of the New Hebrides group, which lie between New Caledonia and the Solomons. Into this no man's land (which, had the Japs only known our weakness, would have fallen easily to them) we placed selected small units, all that we then had available, to establish at least the beginnings of naval bases, air fields, and depots. The work was unpublicized although there is little doubt that the Japs with their well-established spy system and their relative freedom for aerial observation were, at the time, well aware of much of what went on. But, back in the States, it seemed as if the Navy were standing still, as if there were no answer to the question, "Where is our fleet?"

52

Finally, with the August 7 landings on Guadalcanal and Tulagi, the American public and the world learned that our fleet *was* "in being" and our Marines were on the march. But the picture they got was a distorted one, for they could not see the thin, essential chain of, as yet, half-built bases which stretched back from Guadalcanal.

One of the most advanced of these was on the island of Espiritu Santo, the northernmost of the New Hebrides. Here in midsummer of 1942, we had landed five hundred troops with five hundred rifles, somewhat optimistically termed a "holding force." They were followed by other units which arrived in driblets—engineers, construction men, and airmen.

And then, on August 11, five days after the start of the battle of Guadalcanal, a ship entered the harbor carrying a medical detachment under the command of Captain Joel J. White. On deck, Captain White had seventeen medical officers and two hundred corpsmen. In the hold, buried beneath a welter of other supplies, was the equipment for a two-hundred bed mobile hospital.

This unit had originally been destined for Tulagi in the Solomons. But as the battles in that region progressed, it became apparent that the time was too early for the establishment of so large a hospital around Guadalcanal. On August 19, one week after their arrival at Espiritu Santo, Captain White was ordered to establish his unit at that harbor.

Fortunately, their week of waiting had been spent in surveying the region. The doctors, of what later became a major naval hospital, had already selected a site in the coconut groves near the one tiny, rotting, coconut-log landing stage which was the only dock facility the harbor then offered. On this small pier, where the inter-island freighters once used to make their infrequent stops to pick up copra and to drop supplies, the hospital corpsmen and the doctors-turned-long-shoremen began to land their equipment. It came up out of the hold in a wild jumble of odds and ends, the corrugated sheet metal of Quanset huts mixed in with cases of pharmaceuticals, bedding, tentage, and mosquito netting.

From the ramshackle dock, a single wagon trail led along the shore to the site of the new hospital. This site was by no means ideal. It was on low land in the lee of a hill down which, with every rain, coursed a series of minor torrents. Yet, at the time, it was the only spot which could have been selected, the only area to which patients could have been brought from the new air-strip, which was just being completed, and from the Navy landing.

By August 25, when they had two huts barely roofed over and filled with cots, they received their first patients, eighty-seven desperately wounded men, flown in by air from Guadalcanal. Most of them were so badly injured that it is doubtful whether they would have survived the few additional hours of air journey which would have brought them to the next hospital then in operation, nearly five hundred miles down the line.

And so, amidst the clatter of hammering and in a sea of mud, Joel White's hospital came into being—a hospital that was literally built round its patients. On the next day, and every day thereafter for months to come, new groups of wounded men were flown in and new huts were ready, or at least ready enough, to receive them. Frequently, the beds had to be placed so close together that the corpsmen could not pass between them. But, somehow or other, every last patient that was thrown upon this hospital was cared for.

The hospital at Espiritu Santo *was* Joel White, although he would be the last to admit it. It reflected the man's character. Its faults were his faults; its strength was his strength.

Captain White was a regular Navy man, typical of the best which the Navy Medical Corps has produced. He was

one of a sizable group of the 1917 graduates of the Vander-
bilt University Medical School who entered the Navy at the
beginning of the first World War. Like Captain Bryan of the
Relief, he had served on the *Oklahoma,* the old battleship
which seems to have been a post-graduate proving ground for
dozens of naval surgeons. After the war he stayed on with
the Navy, living the quiet and rather uneventful life of a
fleet doctor, rising gradually through the ranks and raising
a family, three boys and a girl.

He was close to the retirement age when this war started;
a graying, unimpressive little man, past middle age, whom
one would have thought best suited for a desk job at some
quiet post back home. But then something happened to this
quiet man, something which changed him, overnight, into a
sleepless force whose only goal—to listen to the legends that
have sprung up about him—was to get and to treat more
patients and still more and still more.

That something was the loss of his eldest son. The boy
had graduated from the University of Pennsylvania, winning
highest honors in engineering. Methodical Captain White
had planned for him, in some detail, the successive steps of a
civilian engineering career. Like all men who have followed
the sea, Joel White dreamed of the land as a rosy place.
While he knew that he would never settle down to run a
chicken farm, his dreams expressed themselves in the plans
he drew for his son, plans for a non-military career ashore.

Then, shortly after his graduation, the boy enlisted in the
Field Artillery and Joel White's plans, as have so many
others, went up in smoke. And yet he was glad, because of
all the branches of the military service, the artillery is closest
to engineering. He may even have dreamed of rebuilding his
plans and setting his son on the selected path as soon as the
emergency was over. But that dream too was shattered, for
the boy died on duty.

All this Joel White did not tell me. I learned it much later from friends of his in Washington, friends who watched the man as he went about his duties in a daze, friends who thought of him—for a while—as a shattered man, hardly fit for the rough duty the Medical Corps was meeting and preparing to meet in the tropics. Yet, it was to these friends, some of them his superior officers, that Joel White appealed for an assignment outside the States. And it was these men who, with the insight into character which is the essence of good psychiatry, decided to give Joel White his wish. They had no illusions that he would forget the lost boy, no matter where they sent him. But somehow they knew that he could not sit still, that he would break up and disintegrate unless he could get to work, unless he could throw himself into some fight. For Joel White, that fight consisted in seeing to it that other people's boys came home, that other men's sons lived to go on to fulfill their fathers' dreams after the war.

I can picture Dr. White reading this. I can see his thin, lined face pucker up and I can hear him say, "Rubbish, sentimental rubbish." For I doubt whether, even to himself, Dr. White would quite admit that this is precisely what happened—although his friends swear it is so.

But whether or not the details are correct, the man I found and the man I heard about all over the South Pacific, fitted into this picture. Some doctors (particularly those who did not know him well) criticized him. They said he was obsessed by numbers, that he tended to neglect the individual in his overpowering desire to serve the mass. And when I first saw his squalid hospital, knee-deep in mud under the dripping coconut trees, I was inclined to give credence to this view.

But other men told me the other side of the story—how important it had been to provide some kind of treatment, even minimal treatment, for the thousands of men who were brought down to Espiritu Santo in those first few desperate weeks. I began to see that Joel White was right, dead right, and that his critics were in the wrong. I began to understand the meaning of each unfinished hut, to realize that his swampy, shanty-town of a hospital had actually accomplished a far greater job than it possibly could have done had it been directed by anyone who placed greater importance upon hospital procedures or surgical traditions and less importance upon doing the best he could with what he had available.

When the flood of patients began, the amateur long-shore-men had succeeded in landing only a small proportion of the hospital equipment. Most of their huts were in the bottom of the ship's hold buried under tons and tons of other supplies. So Captain White and his fellow doctors turned to the other units which had already landed and to the new groups which were coming in all the time. They begged and borrowed—and in some cases, it is rumored, they stole—housing of every sort, lugging it away piecemeal from the shore in their jeeps and even carrying whole sections of little buildings by hand to get them erected in time for new groups of patients.

Almost from the start they had their first operating room in order and their three surgeons worked in relays on the cases that came in each morning on the planes from Guadalcanal.

They got their first break on August 30, when the hospital ship *Solace* put into port and took off ninety of their patients. By then the roster had swelled to close to three hundred patients and even the relief given them by the *Solace* only served to reduce the rolls to the capacity originally contemplated for the hospital. This figure, two hundred beds, was based however on the sum total of their equipment and nearly half of that was still in the hold of their ship.

And yet from day to day they took more patients and the hospital grew, spreading out, it seemed aimlessly, through the coconut grove. The huts were placed at least ninety feet apart, for at that time a mass Jap air raid on Espiritu Santo was a distinct possibility and a token raid by a few planes had actually been attempted. This dispersal, although essential, added greatly to the staff's difficulties for it served to spread the hospital over a tremendous area with lakes and seas of mud between each ward.

By October 1, the unit was in full commission with all its equipment on the site. But by October 10, its actual capacity—as measured by its patient roll—had reached four hundred. In late October, the daily census was running between five and six hundred. Corpsmen would work all morning erecting huts, building paths, installing the laundries, and galleys and laboratories. Then they would turn-to, about noon, to receive the daily load of patients which the ambulances brought down from the airfield. They would work to make these men comfortable—often in huts which had been roofed over but a few hours before—until far into the night, catching their own sleep, what there was of it, in their blanket rolls on the ground. For the beds and cots intended for the staff had of course long since been turned over to the patients.

Somehow, though, as the weeks wore on, the unit began to catch up with its work. By late October it was renamed the Hospital Section of the Advanced Naval Base, a title which merely recognized the fact that it was not only treating cases arising from Guadalcanal and from the fleet, but was also carrying the growing load of casualties which developed among the fast-mounting personnel of the post.

By November, the daily average of patients had risen to seven hundred and at the turn of the year the unit had a capacity of eight hundred patients, six hundred in beds, and two hundred more on cots.

✦

Meanwhile, however, Joel White was not satisfied. On September 30, he took three of his doctors and eighteen corpsmen and flew up to Guadalcanal where they established an advanced evacuation unit of sixty beds. A few weeks later he installed a forty-bed unit on Tulagi, further depleting his none too large staff.

His fellow officers began to joke about it. They talked of Joel White going out "to sell subscriptions" and accused him, jokingly, of trying to line up his patients even before they were hit. Some called him a "long-distance ambulance chaser."

But beneath all their jokes one felt a note of admiration and of deep loyalty. For never have I seen a man so able to inspire devotion—quietly and without seeming to seek it—among those who worked under him.

Some doctors who were sent to Captain White's hospital couldn't fit in at all. Everything about the place—the slap-dash manner in which it was run, the constant, grinding pressure, the woefully inadequate living quarters—ran counter to their civilian habits. These men soon disappeared, going back to the neater and the more orderly hospitals in the south or securing assignments on ships where everything, one could be certain, would at least be shipshape.

Those who remained cursed the skipper, called him a slave-driver, complained and griped and belly-ached. But they wouldn't have left their mud-flat for any other post in the Navy and they stood ready—singly or en masse—to defend Joel White against all comers.

Situated as they were, closest to the fighting front, White's surgeons received many of the most urgent cases, particularly the men wounded in the great naval battles of September, October, and November of 1942. To them were brought the casualties from the aircraft carrier *Wasp*, which went down in the vicinity of the Solomons on September 15, 1942. In their three operating theaters were treated the majority of the wounded from the battle of Savo Island in November. Up to January, 1943, fully 80 per cent of the hospital's cases were in the surgical classification—hundreds of fractures, chest wounds, head wounds, and abdominal injuries of the most severe and complex types. With the coming of 1943 and the final victory in Guadalcanal, the character of the hospital's patients changed. Fully 90 per cent of the patients in the spring of 1943 were medical cases, men with malaria, dengue, dysentery, and the tropical fungus infections common to the area.

Yet, though the urgency of the individual cases was no longer as great as it had once been, the need for this hospital continued to be acute and the influx of patients remained at a high rate. In nine months the unit handled approximately thirteen thousand men, most of them either severely wounded or seriously ill. Of this number ten thousand were eventually evacuated to the rear and the remainder were returned to their units fit for duty.

Even when I arrived at Espiritu Santo—when the base that started with five hundred soldiers had grown to be a great bastion of the fleet—this hospital was still bearing a major part of the load. I remember sitting in the general office while awaiting the return of Joel White from one of his countless side trips. The yeomen were tallying up their daily census of patients, deducting the men who were being discharged back to duty and adding onto the rolls those admitted within the last twenty-four hours. When they finished their tally, one looked up and remarked happily, "Say, we're really getting somewhere. We are only twenty-one over capacity."

✦

As our forces in the South Pacific grew in the spring of 1943, the Medical Corps was able to cease its catch-as-catch-can operations and to plan its further expansion on a much more orderly and far-sighted basis. New hospital units were carefully formed and trained in the States. Advance parties were sent out to prospect for sites. Engineering groups planned water systems, laid miles of mains, felled trees, and leveled the ground, even before the ships which bore the hospital equipment arrived on the scene. When the doctors and the corpsmen of these new units did reach a site, they had more than the week which was given to Joel White to get down to work.

One such hospital unit reached Espiritu Santo last spring under the command of Captain Lucius W. Johnson, another old-time Navy doctor. Captain Johnson was particularly well fitted for the task that had been set him, to build a permanent hospital of a thousand beds or more at Espiritu Santo. For, in the fall of 1940, he had pioneered the technique of mobile hospital construction, developing the Navy's Mobile Base Hospital, Number 1, at one of our new Caribbean bases. The Surgeon General, Rear Admiral McIntire, had managed to secure from Congress an appropriation for what was, in that day, a radical experiment and—under Captain Johnson—all the thousand and one bugs, which any such large project must entail, were ironed out. A dozen types of tents and pre-fabricated buildings were tested. Special portable laundry equipment, commissary equipment, x-ray and operating room facilities, and innumerable other appurtenances, were manufactured and tried out and broken down and re-assembled and found wanting and rebuilt again. Thus, more than a year before this country entered the war, the Navy had learned—by doing—the delicate and infinitely complex art of moving an entire hospital, with its personnel, on to any beach in the world and setting it quickly in operation without dependence on outside aid or outside facilities.

In Espiritu Santo, Captain Johnson's advance party had selected an ideal site, where the coconut groves topped a high ridge that would be more nearly free from mud and mosquitoes than any other spot on the island. Here his seventy-five doctors and seven hundred corpsmen turned to and laid out a veritable city.

The standard barrel-shaped, corrugated-metal wards were rearranged in a three-winged "T" formation, so that a single central building could be erected (where the three wards converged) as an entry, office, emergency operating, and treatment room and general service center. These buildings were connected—to each other and to the vast mess halls, laundries, x-ray laboratories, offices, and surgical centers—by a series of well-constructed coral paths and covered board-walks. Cul-de-sac roadways were carefully planned so that the ever-churning jeeps would not be able to turn the entire area into a quagmire. Adequate cottages and barracks were erected to house the doctors, the technicians and the corps-men.

When I visited this great hospital, while it was still in the process of erection, I could not help but compare it with Captain White's poor, dilapidated huts down on the beach. This would certainly be a far better place to be sick in. Here, certainly, men would stand a better chance of recovery. Here, at last, would be a real hospital in the tropics.

But Captain Johnson, as if reading my thoughts, sought to correct my point of view. "Yes," he said, "we are going to have a beautiful hospital here when we get through with it. But don't forget that we would never have had the time to build this place if it had not been for old Joel White, down the hill there. He and his doctors and corpsmen are the ones who have really built this hospital, because they held the fort and handled the load while we have been taking our time up here."

It was then that I remembered something that Joel White had shown me the first day I met him—the blueprints of a hospital that was never built. For White, too, had looked forward to the day when he could get out of the muck. He and the officers under him had planned a hospital, an ambitious unit with a fine water supply, with company streets and mudless lawns and well-spaced buildings.

But, somehow, every time things let up just a little bit and it seemed as if they might get down to building their new hospital, some ship had turned in with forty or fifty wounded or a new flurry of fighting on Guadalcanal had brought another hundred or two hundred patients into the shambles on the shore. And so Joel White rolled up his well-worn plans again and devoted himself and his men to the day-to-day task of caring for each day's wounded.

Somehow you felt that Dr. White was right in leaving the building of the rear-line hospital to another man. And at the same time you couldn't help but feel that thirteen thousand men were lucky indeed that a man with the temperament of a "glorified ambulance chaser" had happened to be on the spot in the months when there was neither time nor means nor labor to build a "good" hospital—in the months when anything that kept the rain out was a building.

For there are some men—and Joel White is among them—who can triumph over their surroundings. Any log was a university if Mark Hopkins sat at one end of it and a student at the other. And, quite as truly, any shack will be a hospital if Joel White can find patients to treat there.

CHAPTER V

ENGINES IN AND PATIENTS OUT

ON August 23, 1942, fourteen two-motored Douglas transport planes took wing from a west coast base. As they made altitude and headed out to sea, the Navy began to write a new chapter in its medical history. For these planes, the advance echelon of Marine Air Group Number 25, were headed for the South Pacific to undertake the first major airplane evacuation assignment in support of any of our armed forces.

The few who witnessed their departure would not have thought of them as ambulance planes. Their wings and fuselages were camouflaged in the same tropic patterns used by all our planes in the South Pacific. They bore no special markings. Within their holds one could see little equipment of a medical nature. Only those familiar with such things might have guessed their purpose if they saw the small folding stretcher brackets set tightly, now, against the upper walls to make more room on the outward flight. Nor did the personnel of this squadron suggest its future, for of all the officers they carried—as crews and as passengers—only one was a flight surgeon. The weight restrictions, made necessary by their prolonged flight, held medical equipment down to a bare seventy-eight pounds.

In four or five daringly extended hops, these land planes winged down the long island chains to New Caledonia. On September 1, the tired pilots settled the planes, one after another, on an airport runway at that growing base. The flight-weary service crews climbed out of the crowded cabins,

stretched their tired limbs, unloaded their tools, and immediately began to tune up the motors. The very next morning
these planes made their first flight into the combat zone.

And hardly too early at that, for the battle was well under
way at Guadalcanal—under way and going none too well.
Casualties were piling up in the shell-torn coconut groves,
casualties in desperate need of hospitalization. And evacuation by sea had become increasingly difficult with each passing day. Some of the men, the most urgent cases, were being
taken out—on a catch-as-catch-can basis—on whatever planes
were available for the flight toward the south. But when the
first planes of what was to become the great SCAT Evacuation Service turned up at Henderson Field, in the early
morning of September 3, the harassed Marine doctors there
breathed a sigh of relief, knowing that now, for the first time
in weeks, they could offer their emergency cases something
more than just a fighting chance for survival.

During those first six weeks, the service depended almost
entirely upon hospital corpsmen. There was no opportunity
for regular medical supervision of the loading of the planes
at Guadalcanal. Instead, the medical officers of each fighting unit made what arrangements they could to bring the
most desperate of their cases up to the field at flight time.
The single doctor who had accompanied the planes across the
Pacific flew time and again with twenty and twenty-five acute
cases, while in the other planes hospital corpsmen did their
best to provide for the patients during the four, five, or seven
hour flights.

Early in October, the squadron's medical personnel arrived in force and adequate medical equipment came in by
surface ship. By the middle of the month, a second squadron
of twelve planes came through and SCAT began sending
five planes a day up the line, taxing its equipment to the
mechanical limit of safety and beyond, but getting the

wounded out. By November 1, a sufficiently large number of medical officers was available to provide at least one flight surgeon on every day's run. By that time, too, the ground forces had set up reception services on an adequate scale so that patients could be classified at Guadalcanal, so that space could be budgeted among the various fighting units, and so that the men who were flown out could be placed most expeditiously into the wards and operating rooms of the hospitals in New Caledonia and the New Hebrides.

Meanwhile SCAT—the South Pacific Combat Air Transport Command—was doing yeomen's work of another sort. For its planes—which could expect no recognition as ambulance craft from the Japanese—had a two-way job to do. On the outward run they carried the sick and the wounded, but on the flights up to Guadalcanal they were free to carry anything they could bring in. That meant new propellers, engine parts, and emergency repair tools. It also meant airplane mechanics and other skilled specialists. At one time, when things were at their very worst around Henderson Field, it even meant bringing in aviation gas to ensure that the fighters protecting the field might go aloft the next day.

In those early days, neither the pilots nor the doctors had much in the way of precedent to go by. Evacuation of the wounded by air had long been contemplated by the armed forces of all nations. Both the Army and the Navy had developed experimental air evacuation planes a number of years back. But these planes had never been tested in combat. When they had been used at all they were used under peacetime conditions, when everything could be controlled and when risks could be held to the irreducible minimum.

The doctors who worked on these experimental planes were cautious in the extreme. Their reports warned against every imaginable contingency. They told of the dangers of carrying, at high altitudes, patients suffering from acute appendicitis, intestinal obstructions, peritonitis, strangulated hernias, or wounds of the abdomen. They warned that, unless oxygen was provided, patients with wounds of the circulatory system or with lung injuries would suffer intensely unless carried at extremely low altitudes. They pointed out that men with infections of the sinuses or of the middle-ear could not tolerate even small changes of altitude without a great deal of pain and aggravation of the disease process. They warned particularly against the effect of flight on the emotional state of the neurotic patient.

Most of these warnings had a sound basis in experience and in theory. But of necessity they had to be largely ignored in the face of the only alternative, which would have been to leave a high proportion of the most desperately wounded to die in the shambles around Henderson Field. So the doctors of SCAT took their chances. They held them down to a minimum by taking every precaution available to them. They flew low over the water when that was possible. They gave oxygen to patients who seemed to need it. They "snowed under," with morphine, the more acute psychiatric cases. And yet, though they minimized chances by these precautions, they were acutely conscious of the fact that they *were* taking chances.

But somehow their worst fears failed to materialize. Day after day the planes came in with all their patients in good condition. Day after day the predicted troubles failed to materialize. Months passed before a single patient died in the air and months passed again before the record was marred by a second death. And during all that time thousands upon thousands of battle weary men walked or were carried with blood-stained bandages onto the mercy planes which flew them to safety.

All this I knew, before I ever rode a SCAT plane, for the story of this airline had become a medical legend in the South

Pacific. But it was only after I had ridden the planes a half-dozen times and had come to know the amazing doctors and corpsmen and nurses and pilots who made a dream come true—only then did I begin to appreciate fully the vast scope of the life-saving miracle these people had accomplished.

My first contact with SCAT was not an auspicious one. Lieutenant Frank Rounds, the young Washington newspaperman who handled press relations for the Navy at Espiritu Santo, had arranged for my flight authorization and priority. Together we drove out to the air-strip. There, in the SCAT Operations hut, he introduced me to the local officer in charge, a Marine captain named Jaeckle. It should have been Hyde.

Rounds, in his conscientious way, explained the purpose of my trip. But then he made a mistake. "If you can arrange it, Captain," he said, "Mr. Maisel would like to fly up on a plane carrying a nurse."

The tall, leather-faced marine, who had been busy till then with a game of Chinese checkers, turned for the first time to give us his full attention. He looked us both over with a glare that singed our hair and made the sweat boil off our steaming faces with a sizzle. The big veins in his neck stood out and he turned a brilliant purple. He looked us over and then he turned away and very deliberately spat through the doorway.

Then at last he spoke, spilling out a torrent of vituperation that made everyone in the large room turn around. It turned poor Frank Rounds white under his sunburn and left me standing there open-mouthed and dazed.

"So he wants to see a nurse, does he?" he began. "Just like all these other ——— ——— correspondents, he wants to see a pretty nurse. He isn't interested in the guys who really did the job. No. The corpsmen don't count. They don't make

good pictures. Nobody cares how hard they work. Nobody
cares what chances they take. Nobody cares if they live or
they die. We used to be happy here, just flying our planes.
And now what happens? Some damned jerk of a Hollywood
genius back in Washington gets a brainstorm and sends us
a flock of G. I. females. And right off the bat every ———
——— newshound in the South Pacific turns up and wants
to take their pictures. Why don't you bastards learn to tell
the truth for a change . . . ?"

It must have taken five minutes before any of us quite
caught the drift of the captain's spiel. Then it took fifteen
more before he ran out of breath and we could work a word
in edgewise. By that time I was breathless from just trying.
Neither Rounds nor I managed to muster all the cutting answers we thought up later. At the moment all I could do was
explain that I really wanted to see the patient and that I
didn't particularly care who rode on the plane up to Guadalcanal as long as I could ride on it coming out.

That calmed the captain down a bit but not much. After
a slight second flurry—slight by comparison with the first
typhoon of words—he said something about picking any bunk
I wanted in the transient camp across the road and being
called in time for breakfast and a 3:00 A.M. take-off.

I followed Frank out of the hut and we started to lug my
bag and portable typewriter down the road, Rounds getting
angrier and angrier with every step. Then, just as the lieutenant was about to turn back and start the fight all over
again, we each felt a hand on our shoulders. It was one of
the other men who had been working in the hut, a Marine
lieutenant. "Don't let the skipper get your goat," he said
soothingly. "You just made the mistake of being the um-
teenth guy to come out here this week to see the females.
You caught hell for all of them. And don't think we have
really got anything against these girls. They have a lot of

guts and they'll probably do a good job. It's just that the old-timers around here know what a job the corpsmen have done. They hate to see the boys who carried the load get slighted."

Pacified, we walked on and soon I was in my bunk and Frank took his jeep back to headquarters. In the mess-hall in the transient camp the flying officers lined up with their trays and took their suppers and downed their atabrin pills and glared a bit at the two nurses who were already seated with their plane crews at a table in the corner. The boy directly in front of me, a short curly-haired blond, seemed to glare harder than the rest. Every once in a while he muttered a bit and turned away. Then his eyes would veer again back to the table where the girls sat and he would glare again and mutter some more. When we had filled our trays we both sat down at the same table and I asked him why nobody seemed to like the nurses.

"Hell," he answered. "It's nothing personal. It's just that two women among a thousand men don't do anyone any good." He smiled at the idea and added, "It would be easier to have none at all. Then we could just atrophy in peace."

Back in the dormitory, I found an unused cot and racked up for what was left of the evening. Two or three times during the night, the truck drove up to the door and a marine with a flashlight came into the hut and played it on the cots, until he found the man he wanted. Then one or more would get up and quietly put on their shoes—we all slept in our clothes—and go out into the night. A few minutes later, there would be a roar overhead and another plane would circle around, until its sound grew faint and we all fell asleep again.

At three, it was my turn. In the mess hall I was introduced to the SCAT crews who were to make the flight. We all sat around stoking up with scrambled dehydrated eggs and black coffee. After a bit, a weapons-carrier drew up. The flyers threw in their little leather bags and we climbed in and drove out to the field.

Three planes were warming up on the apron and we stood around to have a last smoke in the warm wash of their props. The two nurses stood off by themselves until we got the signal to climb in. Then they separated and the tall, blond one entered my plane.

Most of the rest of the passengers were New Zealanders, shorter than our men and with the ruddy, smiling faces which they seem to breed in New Zealand. As soon as we took off, the nurse went to the compartment at the rear of the cabin and brought out blankets which she handed to the boys, seated in two rows on the folding aluminum troughs that ran down each side of the plane. On the cabin floor the boys had thrown their barracks bags and helmets, forming a great waist-high pile that ran from the auxiliary gas tanks up forward all the way to the end of the cabin.

Soon the pilot trimmed his engines and we settled down to the steady drive through the night. Some of the men lay down on the pile of bags, managing to sleep in unbelievably awkward positions. Others napped, half erect in their seats, while a few squirmed to look out of the windows at the inky emptiness down below.

I went up forward and introduced myself to the nurse. She had heard about the incident in Operations and she wanted to tell her side of the story. There wasn't much to tell; simply that she was one of twenty-six nurses who had been sent out there to do a job and that she was doing it, and that she couldn't help it if they hadn't been sent out earlier.

Even in her ugly flying overalls, Ruth Barnes was a pretty girl, a honey blonde with deep brown eyes. She said her piece quietly, with dignity, as if she just wanted to get it on the record. Then she dismissed the subject and tried to make it seem unimportant. Only her eyes showed the hurt which she was carrying, not just for herself but for the entire group of nurses.

I asked her about her background. She was twenty-four years old, from Reynolds, a little village in Illinois of five hundred, filled with retired farmers. She had studied nursing in Rock Island and then stayed on there at a hospital when she graduated in 1940. On August 8, 1942—the day after our landings in the Solomons—she had enlisted in the Army Nurses Corps "for the duration and six months." Then came five months of nursing at Chanute Field followed by an intensive five week course in tropical medicine at Beaumont Field, near Louisville. After that, she and the twenty-five others were flown out to the Pacific and assigned—just a few weeks before—to the SCAT run.

She wasn't an ardent feminist. In fact, I doubt if Lieutenant Barnes would have recognized the word. But she just couldn't see—just couldn't understand why some of the men —"only a few," she said—insisted on treating the girls as different. "I guess we'll just have to wait until they get used to us. Once they think of us as fixtures, everything will go all right."

Only a few days later, one of the new nurses saved the lives of a co-pilot and navigator when their plane, flying without passengers, was wrecked. After that, in all of the rest of my time in the Pacific, I never heard anything but praise for the SCAT nurses. They had become, as Ruth Barnes had hoped, "fixtures."

After a time it grew intensely cold in the plane which had climbed to eight thousand feet. The nurse got up and found me a blanket and we both settled down for a nap. Throughout the cabin the men slept, seemingly as unconcerned as if we were on a pullman back in the States.

Then the sun began to come up red out of the sea, burning the ground mist off until we could see islands down below us. Soon we were over San Cristobal, the easternmost of the Solomons chain, a rugged, mountainous mass of jungle over which the eye searched unsuccessfully for the slightest sign of human habitation. Away to either side, stretched an endless, empty waste of sea, glistening in the morning sun. Far off over the wing-tip we could make out the higher mountains which were Guadalcanal. The pilot throttled down our motors and we began the long glide into Henderson Field.

As we came in over the bloody island, it too seemed to be an endless waste, except along the winding shores where, here and there, a coconut plantation seemed to hang on at the edge of the jungle as if to resist being pushed into the sea. Off to the left was a crescent of mountains, towering above us now and enclosing the flat coastal shelf which made Guadalcanal an ideal air base, worth fighting for. To the right and far ahead we could make out tiny Gavutu and Tulagi, nestling up against Florida Island.

Then suddenly our plane heeled into a sharp bank and everyone awoke and peered through the windows. Far below we could make out a tiny floating object. The pilot must have thought it was a rubber boat, adrift with castaways, for he spiraled over it until we were low enough to see it clearly. Then we all saw that it was a native canoe with a huge yellow sail. In those waters, where so many ships had fought and men had drowned, we watched two nonchalant native boys idly dragging their toes in the water. Even our swooping plane caused no consternation among them. Planes were old stuff to them by now.

We leveled off and headed up the coast past Koli point and on towards a great figure eight that lay like a scar on the green earth, between the jungle and the coconut trees. Soon the land was rushing up at us and we roared down the

runway and bumped to a stop. We stepped out onto Henderson Field and stretched our legs, and a great cloud of
dust rose up to greet us while squadrons of planes raced their
motors on all sides as they prepared for an early morning
bombing mission.

It was weeks later, after I had gone on to Tulagi and to
the Russell Islands and then returned to Guadalcanal, that
I looked up Lieutenant Ralph Bookman at the SCAT operations terminal at Henderson Field. The headquarters were
an unimpressive little huddle of huts and wood-floored tents,
set out in the open, some distance from the main runway.
To one side was a small galley and mess hall, a post office
tent and a general office. The other two sides of the U-shaped
compound consisted of weather-worn tents and two or three
bungalows which seemed to have been made of driftwood
carefully hauled in from the beach.

In one of the tents I found Dr. Bookman busily engaged
in introducing another lieutenant, Dr. M. W. Woolcott, to
the intricacies of SCAT operations. Both men were lying on
their cots as I came in from the pouring rain. Once I had
explained the purpose of my visit they motioned me to a
third cot, providing a chair on which I might throw my dripping shoes and socks and cap and shirt. Stripped to the waist,
and reclining, one felt relatively cool—cool enough at any
rate to carry on a conversation.

Both of the doctors were extremely young. Bookman, a
New Yorker, had graduated from the Long Island College
of Medicine in 1939. A year later he had entered the Navy,
receiving his flight training at the great air center at Pensa-
cola. Guadalcanal had been his first assignment in the South
Pacific and now—after five or six months—Dr. Woolcott had
come up the line to relieve him.

Woolcott was even younger, a graduate of the University

of Pennsylvania Medical School, class of 1941. Yet, like so
many of the young officers I met in the Pacific, he had married before leaving for overseas duty. His wife back in Mans-
field, Ohio, he told me, was expecting a baby "any day now."

Lying there in their shorts, these doctors seemed to be
mere boys, yet they had already acquired that quiet competence which service with the Navy seems to build quickly
into a man. I could not help but think, watching them, that
in a way, they were fortunate to be at Guadalcanal. For here
they were seeing more medicine and getting more practice, in
a few months, than ordinarily comes to men of their age
in many years at home.

Ralph Bookman deprecated his job. "I'm not really practicing medicine here," he said. "I'm just a glorified des-
patcher. All I have to do is to find out how many seats and
stretcher berths I am going to have available each morning
and then spread them out among all the dispensaries and
unit hospitals on the island. Then, just when I have got my
schedules nicely worked up, something always happens and
instead of getting four stretchers and twenty sitters we are
likely to find twenty stretchers and only four sitters."

"Is that really all you do here?" I asked.

"Well, no, not quite all," he answered. "You see, we try
to get the planes off the run-way an hour or two before dawn.
But patients keep dribbling in here all night—sometimes
even a day or two before they are due to leave. That means
we have to run a sort of hospital-hostel here. Then it's up to
us to decide whether the men are fit to fly. Most of the time
that doesn't take much deciding. The doctors who send the
men to us know pretty well by now whether they are our
type or not. But every once in a while it calls for a fairly tick-
lish decision. We know we *might* kill a man by putting him
on the plane and at the same time we know we might kill
him by refusing him a passage. We have to make some de-

cision and then we worry about it till we get a flash back from the base that the loads have arrived safely.

I began to quiz the doctors about their corpsmen. Immediately the conversation perked up. Both Woolcott and Bookman had been slow to talk about themselves but there was no hesitancy to mar their praise of the enlisted men who worked under them. One after another, stories tumbled from their lips, tales of the heroism of the Navy's male nurses, of the period which Bookman nostalgically referred to as the "good old days," when Guadalcanal was a battlefield and the Japs were just over the hill. One tale in particular impressed me, for it typified the nonchalance with which these unarmed kids had carried on their day-to-day work, performing acts far beyond the explicit demands of duty without any thought of recognition and reward.

It was the story of a night on which three planes, bulging with badly injured stretcher cases, were waiting on the runway apron for a take-off. The Japanese had filtered onto the far end of the field and, from the planes, the worried officers could see the constant flash of tracer bullets a few hundred yards away. Overhead they could hear the drone of Jap planes. The last hour of darkness was ticking away and with dawn a safe get-away would become impossible for the unarmed transports. Unless they took off immediately the Jap would almost surely catch them long before they made altitude and left the southern tip of Guadalcanal behind.

But, with the fighting going on so close by and with planes overhead, it was impossible to throw on even the dim runway guide lights. So the pilots huddled in a group and talked things over and couldn't think of anything to do. Meanwhile, each time they stared at their watches, a few more of the precious minutes of darkness had passed away.

Just then, a corpsman, who had brought up a jeep-load of patients from some dispensary down on the beach, realized that something was wrong. Perhaps he overheard the pilots talking. Or perhaps he sized the situation up for himself with that second sense which every man on Guadalcanal seemed to develop—that intuition about airplanes and airfields that told even boys who were not flyers just what was wrong and what to do about it. Without an order the kid hopped into his jeep, threw her into gear and ran her, without headlights, down the field while the dazed flyers and physicians watched him in bewilderment.

When he got into the midst of the flying bullets, half a mile away at the end of the runway, they saw his red brake-light flash on and off and in Morse code they read his signal, "Take off, dammit, take off."

Major Owen Ross was the first to realize exactly what was happening. He hopped into his cockpit and without warming up his engines, threw the throttles wide open. In the blast of his propellers the men who were to stay behind had barely time enough to take down the ladder and close the wide cabin doors. Then he was off the apron and lurching down the runway, high-tailing it toward the little red light that gleamed steadily now at the end of the field.

The other two planes followed, getting under way even before Ross was off the ground. As they passed overhead the tracers, whose lines of fire had been running horizontal until then, mounted upward and everyone saw that the Japs were taking pot shots at the planes. Then the sound of their motors grew dim and the little red light at the end of the field went out. The doctors and the corpsmen and the ambulance drivers stood around their vehicles, waiting for the jeep to come back. But it didn't come. When dawn came the Japs had been driven back into the jungles and the jeep was not to be found.

Ross came up as a passenger on another plane the next day, came up especially to bring a present—a quart of whiskey— for the corpsman. But when he got there no one knew the

kid's name nor his outfit. No one knew for certain whether
this boy, who drove directly into the line of fire and then sat
there with his foot on the brake pedal, had come out alive.
If he made it, he had just driven off and back to his post and
probably caught hell for being so late.

That is, *if* he made it.

It was late that night—after I had had all my papers
put in order up at headquarters and received my precious
flight priority and watched a movie in an open air amphi-
theater just a few hundred yards from the field and caught
a few hours of sleep and found a jeep driver awake enough
and willing to take me out to the field—that I met Dr. Bookman again. Three planes had been brought out from the
revetments and their crews were lounging round under the
wings catching a last bit of shut-eye before the take-off.
Bookman was busily directing the unloading of half a dozen
ambulances which had come shrieking in out of the night
from all directions. His greeting was an apology.

"I did the best I could for you," he said. "But I couldn't
manage to get you any interesting cases to ride with. All we
have got here is a bunch of athlete's feet. You should have
been here in January. You'd have seen cases then that *were*
cases."

As he talked the "athlete's feet" were passing before me
and entering the nearest plane. Four of them were on stretchers covered with blankets so that only their pale faces could
be seen. Two of these had heavy head bandages. A third—
quietly smoking a cigarette as the handlers pushed and
tugged at his stretcher—seemed well enough except for
something strange about the lower part of the blanket which
covered him. One had to look twice to see that it covered
only one leg.

Bookman noticed my stare. "Well," he said, "I'm just

speaking relatively. I guess we get sort of hardened in a job like this. Maybe it's high time Woolcott's come up to relieve me."

The rest of the passengers, the sitters, made their own way into the plane. One or two, with legs in casts, had to be helped up the short ladder. Others hopped in, anxious to get off the ground. One boy lit a cigarette and stood outside the doorway until he had finished his butt and lit another one from it. Then he flipped it away from the plane, shuddered once and raced up the three steps.

Dr. Bookman introduced me to the flight surgeon who was to make the run with us, an Army captain, Harold M. Messenger. Dr. Messenger seemed familiar until I realized that his bright smiling face—crinkly eyes and a perfect set of gleaming white teeth—was an almost exact duplicate of one I had seen many times before in the movies. Messenger would be a lady-killer, if he ever got the time. He, too, was young, younger indeed than Bookman. But, though only thirty, he had already made thirty-five flights such as these. In four months he had treated nearly 750 men in flight, men whose troubles ran the whole gamut—from malaria to war neurosis, from an injured finger to an amputated leg.

The last of the patients were aboard now and the motors of all three planes were warming up, coughing and sputtering as their pilots worked them in for the take-off. I threw my bag and typewriter on board, said good-by to Bookman and Woolcott, and followed Messenger into the plane. Then, just before the doors closed, I turned for one last look at Guadalcanal. All the men on the field around us—the doctors, the corpsmen, the ambulance drivers, and the casuals who seemed to have no particular business there but must have had some reason to be out at 4:00 A.M.—all of them stared at the plane as if they actively and enviously begrudged us our take-off from the war zone. Then one little fellow, standing on the running board of a car, made a thumbs-up sign and one after another the people in the little crowd made the same signal, self-consciously and a little ashamed to show any emotion. I remember wondering how a fellow must feel to watch that scene every night and to know that he wasn't leaving.

Then they turned away, we closed the doors and the plane creaked and droned as we moved off into the runway.

As we climbed above the clouds, Dr. Messenger handed me his passenger manifest and I copied off the list of diagnoses entered in a combination of standard Navy nomenclature and medical shorthand. Here it is, as deciphered for me later.

> Malaria—(five patients)—
> Renal colic and hernia—
> Acute gastritis—
> Amputation, traumatic, left leg—
> Fracture, simple, metatarsal—
> Chronic prostatitis and arthritis—
> T.B., "possible" (for observation)—
> Malnutrition—
> Inguinal hernia—
> Wound, gunshot, head—
> Fracture, left arm—
> Pterygium—
> Ulcer, duodenal—
> Abscess (and malnutrition)—
> War neurosis—(two cases)—
> Dermatosis—
> Jaundice, infectious—two cases

While I worked on my notes, leaning on one of the auxiliary gas tanks on the forward end of the cabin, Dr. Messenger was busy arranging his patients and making them comfortable. Then he came over and sat down.

"Bookman called these spickage," I said. "What do you think of them?"

"It's just an average run," he told me. "I don't think we'll have any trouble with any of them on the way out except, possibly, one of the psychos."

He pointed out an older man, a SeaBee who sat at the other end of the cabin, an unbelievably thin man with a high, balding forehead that seemed to emphasize the deep, black hollows of his eyes. I recalled how, of all the walking patients at the field, this one alone had seemed reluctant—even afraid—to enter the plane. Just as Messenger spoke, the trouble began. We were passing the eastern tip of Guadalcanal and heading over the sea. The sun had not come up yet but it was light enough for us to see the ocean's surface.

As the sea opened out below us, the man Messenger worried about stood up in the center of the cabin. The left side of his face twitched involuntarily and his eyes shifted from side to side, peering out of the windows of the plane. But he stayed carefully to the center as if afraid to go closer to the portholes, as if afraid of the height. He began repeating over and over, in a high-pitched, panic-stricken voice, "There are sharks in that water, there are sharks in that water."

For a moment the tension in that crowded cabin seemed about to reach the breaking point. The sick and battle-worn men moved nervously on the edges of the aluminum seats. Overhead, the stretcher cases craned to see what was happening.

The doctor nudged my arm and I followed him. Rapidly—but with a contagious calmness—he began to question the shrieking man, while I scribbled the answers.

It was hard going at first. The SeaBee's eyes kept shifting jumpily toward the windows and the sun-lit sea far below. And then, his story began to flow until it tumbled from him in a torrent of mixed-up recollections: the memory of terror in two shipwrecks, of a buddy mangled by a shark, of rescue long despaired of.

But as the man spoke, the very telling of his story slowly calmed him down. At length—it may have been twenty minutes later—he sat down. Slowly his face stopped twitching and he buried his head in his hands. The men around us relaxed too. Then Messenger cracked some silly little joke and we all laughed and everyone felt better.

The doctor and I returned to our spot between the auxiliary tanks. There was a wooden framework to hold these tanks in place and a board catwalk down the narrow central passage that led into the forward compartment where the plane's crew worked. We sat on this catwalk, face to face, our feet hanging down at either side among the braces. Messenger was careful to face toward the rear where, looking over my shoulder, he could see everything that was going on among his charges. I asked the doctor whether he often had had trouble with psychoneurotic patients. He told me that they were usually quite quiet; that this man was an exception to the general rule. Often the slightly rarified air at four or five thousand feet served to lull such men into a quiet sleep—sometimes the first normal sleep they had had in weeks. Others, although they kept wide awake, were usually quite able to contain themselves—whether because they knew that now at last they were getting out of the war zone or because the close presence of so many other men in the crowded cabin gave them reassurance, he did not know.

"Occasionally," he told me, "we get a real wild man—but that is very rare. On one trip we had an officer—a major or a colonel, I am not sure I remember which—who had us all in a tight spot for a while. I suppose, because of his rank, he hadn't been watched quite as carefully as most such patients would have been. Once we took off, he stood up at the back of the cabin and reached into the little bag he was carrying—

a neat little, expensive leather overnight kit. I noticed him doing it but all I expected to come out of that bag were some papers or perhaps a handkerchief. Instead he came up with the meanest looking .45 I have ever seen and then very calmly he laid it in the crook of his left arm and held the whole plane up. He ordered us to turn around and go right back to Guadalcanal.

"I was way down the other end of the cabin at the time and when I tried working my way towards him he ordered me to stay back. Most of the rest of the men were too sick to scrap with him, in any event. So, for a while, we all just sat there looking for an opening and hoping he wouldn't let go before we found it.

"Luckily for us, the navigator came through the doorway just then, right behind me. The 'psycho' spotted him immediately and ordered him to go back and have the plane turned around. The kid thought fast and said he would be delighted to do that only he'd have to drop a flare to give them a turning point.

"I never heard of anything like that before. But then neither had the officer with the gun. He fell for it—hook, line, and sinker. He let the navigator come down the entire length of the cabin because he said the flares were in the rear locker. Then when he opened the rear door—behind the man with the gun—he turned and pinned his arms back.

"After that it was all over in a second. The rest of the patients grabbed the pistol and our psycho case was quite ready to sit down and be good. We didn't have to tie him or anything like that. A little while later I was able to give him a glass of water and a sleeping powder. By the time we took him off the plane he was as quiet as a lamb.

"That is the only time," he continued, "that we have had any trouble at all with such cases. Sometimes they will act up a bit but they're usually not the least bit inclined to violence.

We had one man going down the line a few weeks ago who insisted on taking off his shoes and socks. Then he calmly sat down on the floor, tore his orders into little shreds and spent the rest of the trip pouring the paper scraps from one shoe into the other, as if he were working up the foam in a daiquiri.

"It sounds a little disgusting when you retell a story like that. But at the time there was nothing revolting about it and certainly nothing comic. It was just pathetic—as if this poor guy was trying to show the rest of us that he was all washed up and couldn't have stayed with the outfit—trying to justify himself in a desperate, crazy sort of way—but trying nonetheless.

"I got interested in that boy and followed him up a few weeks later. I often do that," Messenger continued, "because you don't get too much medicine riding these planes. Between runs I try to make rounds in the wards at the base or attend conferences at the Army hospital near the field—just to sort of keep my hand in. Well, you may not believe it but this fellow began to straighten out almost as soon as we put him in the hospital. Inside of a couple of weeks—when they had put some fat back on him and cleared up his malaria— he was just about back to normal, as sane and clear thinking as you or I. He recognized me but he didn't have any recollection of what he had done on the plane.

"The funniest thing about it all though—if there is anything funny about such stories—is that I looked up the man's record. Do you know what he was in civil life? A bartender."

While the doctor talked he kept glancing over my shoulder, every once in a while, to make certain that everything was all right among the patients. We had been climbing for a long time now and had reached nearly eight thousand feet. Just as the doctor finished his story, one of our five malaria cases began to have a chill. In the middle of a sentence Messenger sprang into action. An extra stretcher was taken from the rear of the cabin and rigged on the ingenious racks that fold down from the side walls of these airplane ambulances. Blankets were wrapped around the lad and the doctor slipped him a pill. For a few minutes the boy shivered despite the layers of blankets over him. Then the spell passed and he fell off into a quiet sleep.

Messenger left him and went up forward. When he returned to our seat on the catwalk the pilot had nosed the plane down and we went into a long glide to cut the altitude. Dr. Messenger explained that the chill might have been due to come on in any event, but just to be safe he had asked the pilot to seek a lower flight level.

"Most malaria cases do well on the planes," he told me, "much better than we had anticipated in the beginning. But occasionally, when you have to climb over the cloud layer, the rarified air will affect them. You see, malaria destroys the red blood cells, lowers the red cell count. And these red cells in the blood are the ones which carry the oxygen to the system. I think that is why a malarial case is probably a little more sensitive than most men to rarified air. The reduction of their oxygen intake affects a system which already has a lowered oxygen-carrying capacity. Sometimes—though not often—that brings on a premature malarial chill. It isn't dangerous if you take care of it immediately."

We had made our landfall while we talked and the doctor had to leave me to prepare his patients for the ambulance trip. Through the plane windows we could see the jungle coming up at us again—jungle still, but sparser and less terrifying than that of Guadalcanal. Along the shores we saw again the familiar coconut plantations which rim so many of these tropic islands.

Then right below us there passed a tiny island—it couldn't have been more than a few acres—entirely covered with native huts. Somehow these natives have learned that little off-shore islands are free of the malarial mosquito. And thus they sometimes crowd like city dwellers upon a little spot of land where they can be free of the great tropic scourge and where the ocean itself can take care of the major problems of sanitation.

We were flying at tree-top level by now, seemingly headed directly for the jungle itself. Then we winged over in a wide bank and the runway opened out below us, a long white line of coral cut like a gash through the jungle green. We landed and once again the ambulances swallowed up our patients.

More weeks passed—weeks in which I had many opportunities, at the large hospitals, to see the patients the planes had saved—and weeks in which I again rode with SCAT into and out of the combat zones. During all that time one name kept coming up repeatedly, that of Lieutenant Commander Tom T. Flaherty, the medical officer in charge of all SCAT evacuation operations and a man whom all his underlings frankly and effusively worshiped.

When finally I saw Flaherty—like so many of the senior officers in the medical work in the Pacific he was a hard man to find, for he traveled almost constantly—I found him much younger than I had been led to expect, a heavy-set boulder of a man of thirty-three. Although he had received his M.D. from the University of California only in 1937, he had made a reputation for himself in aviation medicine long before he was given his Pacific assignment. He was a "regular," having joined the Navy in 1938. While still a lieutenant he had solved one of the major problems of air training by working out a program for the elimination of air sickness among novice flyers. Every Navy flying trainee today utilizes the Flaherty system or some modification of it to overcome the disorientation, the dizziness and the "stom-ach loop-overs" which once disqualified so many men when they were learning the art of aerial acrobatics.

All this I did not learn from Flaherty himself. Nor did he tell me how he had won the Silver Star for loading his plane and getting off while Jap raiders were strafing Hen-derson Field. I had to get such information from his associ-ates and from his superior officers. For all Flaherty wanted to talk about was SCAT itself—the men who had developed the line with him and the results they had been able to achieve and conclusions they had been able to arrive at.

In his little office—an open corner of the large room where we were constantly interrupted by the friendly greetings of every transient on the post—Flaherty took me through his records and told me of the experiences of other men in solving the scores of problems which had been just theory until SCAT had been created to convert them into practical facts. As he talked one saw nothing of the adventurer in him. If you had not heard about him from others you would have accepted Flaherty as simply a cold, precise, scientific mind—interested more in figures than in people. It was only when we dropped the statistics and others joined us that he loosened up and began—as so many others among the SCAT officers had—to sing the praises of the corpsmen. Flaherty was no fanatic on the subject of nurses. He accepted them on the planes as a logical development of the expanding service. He recognized their skills and the advantages which the mere presence of a woman and a trained nurse could sometimes offer to the patients. And he did not, like some others, misinterpret their willingness to serve under hazard-ous conditions as mere sensationalism.

Yet he was intensely, fervently—almost religiously—loyal to his corpsmen. He told me the story of an incident which had occurred a few days before, the story of one of the few major accidents the SCAT line had met with. This plane, with nineteen patients on board, was forced down by engine trouble. It managed to land on a tiny coral reef half way between the Loyalty Islands and the New Hebrides. The crew beached the plane and lashed it to the coral out-croppings. Then they settled down to await the searchers, while the radio man tried repeatedly to get a signal through. The patients were in charge of a single corpsman and for seven days under the hot sun this lad kept his patients going. The crew gave up their emergency rations, going without food themselves in order not to deprive the patients of their chance for life. The corpsman redressed bandages and ad-ministered drugs and treated the malaria cases while the days passed and their hopes for rescue grew thinner. Luckily their weak signal did get through at last, on the seventh day. But even then they were far from rescue. After more than a week at sea, they were finally found by scout planes and food and fresh water were dropped to them but they still had to spend three more days in the crowded cabin before boats could reach them and take them off.

Yet despite it all every last patient pulled through, thanks once again to a hospital corpsman whose name was not re-membered.

In the beginning, Flaherty told me, the corpsmen had averaged almost two trips a week—more than 110 hours of flying duty for every man every month! Later, when addi-tional personnel was obtained and the pressure let up a bit, they were able to reduce the strain on the corpsmen, hold-ing them down to sixty hours a month. The nurses, Flaherty told me, would do their best work if held to a somewhat lower level—between thirty and forty-five hours a month. Sixty hours in the air had been found the optimum for medi-cal officers.

Most of the early fears about airplane evacuation proved

unfounded. Scores of chest wound cases—once considered the most risky of all for airplane evacuation—were carried with but a single death. Whenever possible, planes carrying such patients are flown at low altitudes, usually at a thousand feet and sometimes even less. The same procedure is followed with men having acute abdominal injuries.

Every effort is made to avoid carrying patients in shock or those who are just recovering from shock. It has been the experience of SCAT however that burned patients, who had received treatment for shock for at least twenty-four hours prior to evacuation, presented no serious problem. Similarly, the doctors discovered that fears which some had held regarding sulfa-treated patients were actually unfounded. Almost every case of gunshot or shrapnel wounds is treated with sulfa drugs prior to evacuation. Yet in not a single instance were any difficulties experienced in carrying such patients.

In one respect, of course, the SCAT operation had a great advantage over similar evacuation services which have since been established in Italy, Africa, and China. For SCAT pilots could usually fly, if it were necessary, at low altitudes. Occasionally, bad weather made this impossible and forced the planes up to seven and even ten thousand feet. But in most instances, their route along the sea lanes permitted flying at as low as five hundred feet.

I asked Flaherty what they thought of the early ambulance planes which had been devised before the war, the experimental planes with pressure cabins and highly specialized equipment. He laughed and said he wondered what would happen to a pressurized cabin if a Jap ever came along and put a hole in it.

He felt that ambulance planes were necessities—in theory. But he reminded me that in most operations—as at Guadalcanal—the need is for transports which can carry a payload in both directions. He pointed to SCAT's record—to the more than ten thousand men they had evacuated—as proof conclusive that frills were not essential for successful evacuation. Flaherty mentioned three essentials—plasma, morphine, and oxygen. Given these and skilled nurses or corpsmen, he felt that the wounded and the sick could always be removed from any war zone.

As he put it, "We know we can evacuate anyone by air unless he is in shock. We're out of the theory stage now. Hell, man, we have carried everything but a pregnancy."

CHAPTER VI

THE RUSSELL ISLANDS

IT was some time after I arrived at Guadalcanal that I decided to try to get into the Russell Islands. At that period these minor islands, sixty miles beyond Guadalcanal itself, were the most advanced outposts we held. Our troops had taken the Russells just about the time I had left the States. But it wasn't until I arrived at Guadalcanal that the first public announcement of our occupation was broadcast although everybody in the Solomons, it seemed, had known all along.

But that is about all they did know. Everything else was quite hush-hush and—as is usually the case—ten rumors replaced every missing fact. Yet it was already apparent that Guadalcanal was no longer a front-line. If I was to see front-line doctors and front-line patients I would have to get into the Russells. So, despite the warnings that I would never make it (which I received from all my friends, of both the press and the Navy), I walked up to headquarters one morning and sought out Lieutenant Eynon, the Flag Secretary.

Bracing myself for a blast, I mumbled meekly, "Do you think we could arrange—sometime when it's convenient— if it isn't too much trouble—for me to get into the Russell Islands?"

Eynon's answer was to turn to a telephone. I don't know just whom he called but he told the voice at the other end, "We would like Mr. Maisel to be provided transportation to the Russells."

Then he turned to me and said, "There will be a sea-plane at the beach at nine o'clock tomorrow morning. Tell them you are the passenger and they will drop you off at Blue Beach."

I gasped, gulped and then fished into my pockets for my papers. I held them out but all Eynon said was, "What is this for?"

"Won't I need an endorsement?"

"Hell, no. They'll figure if you got that far, you must have come on business."

I finally thought of explaining to the lieutenant that I needed the endorsement to convince my wife that I *had* been in the Russells. This won him over and he sat down and dictated an elaborate authorization for travel. Once I got into the islands nobody ever asked to see my papers. They knew I had come up in an American plane and my eyes weren't slanting; that was good enough for them.

In the morning the plane taxied up to the beach as predicted, a two-place scouting job. The pilot said, "Hop in." I scrambled onto a wing, threw my bag and typewriter into the rear cockpit and tumbled in after it just as he took off. A hand came back from the forward cockpit, holding a helmet and pair of goggles. I took off my own *papier-mâché* tropical helmet—a damned poor imitation of the real thing— and tucked it between my legs. Then, while I was putting on the goggles, the plane lurched. My hat fell down and wedged itself in the mechanism of the rudder control. And there it stayed for the rest of the trip. When we finally landed and I told the pilot about it he said, "So that's all it was. And here I'd been worrying about a jammed aileron for twenty minutes."

He must have been pretty glad to get rid of me because, when it came to getting out of the Russells, I couldn't get a plane. The pilot had told all his friends to lay off. So I had to go back, three days behind schedule, by PT boat.

Commander Wissinger, back in Guadalcanal, had told me to look up Lieutenant Commander James E. Goodman, the senior doctor at the SeaBee camp. When I sought him out I found a youngish man, short and thin, with his nose buried deep in a copy of *Guadalcanal Diary*. He asked me if I had read it and when I said yes his next question was, "How did it come out?"

But if Goodman didn't know much about Guadalcanal—his battalion had spent only two days there in transit towards the Russells—he knew his own islands and his own battalion with an intimacy which I have seen in few other men. Through him and through his superior officer, Commander C. L. McGinnis, I got a vivid first-hand picture of the end-less struggle and back-breaking effort involved in hacking an air field out of the jungle.

The battalion—about a thousand men—had been brought up from New Caledonia late in February, 1943. On the way up, its convoy had been attacked by Japanese torpedo bomb-ers. But the SeaBees turned-to and aided the gun crews. In the end all but five of the bombers ran away. Those five were winged and dropped, flaming, into the sea.

At Guadalcanal they unloaded their eleven thousand tons of gear—caterpillars and earthmovers, jeeps and carry-alls, dump trucks and shovels—and transferred them to small landing craft. Meanwhile, a reconnaisance party was sent up to the Russells to find that the Japanese—who had occupied them until they lost Guadalcanal—had either pulled out or back-tracked into the deeper jungles.

Not yet certain which of these alternatives the Japs had followed, the SeaBees embarked, along with defense troops and anti-aircraft groups, for the islands out ahead. The day of their landing the Japs bombed them. They came over again a few days later. But by that time the Construction Battalion had set up gun emplacements and the Japanese were given enough of a pasting to make them stay away for a while.

The SeaBees turned immediately to cutting an air strip across one of the islands. That was their main task, involving the felling of over five thousand coconut trees and the moving of nearly three-quarters of a million yards of sticky gumbo and coral mud. But they also had to build roads and erect camps, not only for themselves but for all the other troops which flowed into the island in a steady stream. The end result was that the SeaBees—as usual—were the last ones to get their own tents erected.

When I asked if they ever hoped to get their huts up they laughed at me and sang snatches of a SeaBee song. It was all about how you "move on again to build some new barracks for our fighting men."

Yet, though everything else was demanding their time and their labor, the SeaBees were not doing as badly as they pretended. They were all construction men at heart and they could make more—out of less material—than any other outfit on earth. In their six weeks in the Russells—in addition to building the air field, the camps and the roads—they had managed to provide themselves with a few conveniences. They had salvaged bricks from the old British copra factory which the Jap bombing had wrecked. With these they built great brick ovens which, every morning, poured out streams of fresh rolls and breads to supply not only their own mess, but those of several other units on the island. They had driven wells deep into the coral and hooked up improvised pumps and built purifiers and great redwood storage tanks. They had set up a communications system—the Russells Telephone and Telegraph Company they called it—and had installed electric lights all over the camp. Their carpenter shops were busy making chairs and tables and floors for the tents, using lumber—fine mahogany—which they had cut in the jungles and ripped into planks on their own portable sawmill.

Meanwhile, from almost any point on the island, you could hear the grinding of their overworked caterpillars and carry-alls, as they clanged away on the air-strip while the rains fell—as much as eleven inches in a week. Long before sunrise the first shift lined up for its chow and moved out to the field, to be followed by portable kitchens which served lunch to the men on the strip itself so that they would lose no time wading through the mud back to camp. The last shift never got back to bed until late at night.

McGinnis was driving his men, driving them hard because that air-strip was important at the time. It would help break up the concentration around Henderson Field and it would provide a fighter take-off point for the bombing of Munda and Bougainville, a point fifteen or twenty minutes nearer to the Japanese than any available spot on Guadalcanal. Fifteen minutes coming and fifteen minutes going adds up to half an hour of extra flying time. And that is a mighty important handful of minutes when you are escorting bombers on a mission. So McGinnis pushed his men and they pushed themselves until more than 70 per cent of their equipment was broken beyond even the SeaBees amazing ability to repair it. That was the job the men had come out to do and no one questioned it.

But it was a job which put a great strain upon the hospital. The strain was all the heavier because the SeaBees (unlike the men on the ships and—especially—unlike the young marines) are an older group of men. The average age of McGinnis's battalion is 34.1 years. Many of the men were volunteers of forty-five and fifty; men who had left families to enlist. Several of them had sons in the Navy or in the Marine Corps. You just couldn't work such men *too* hard.

But at the hospital—a well dispersed group of green tents with a single Quanset hut as a combination x-ray laboratory and operating room—the beds filled up with men whose hearts wanted to work but whose bodies just couldn't take the tropic climate and the work besides. The daily muster at the dispensary ran, at times, as high as 10 per cent of the battalion. Many of the men had malaria, contracted during their short stay on Guadalcanal. Many others had minor injuries, the result of a fumble or a misstep while pushing their machines too hard through the mud. But quite a few had nothing organically wrong with them. They were just dog tired and worn out.

Yet such men were recognized as sick—quite as sick as any of those with a more specific disease. And at the hospital the medics did their best to build them up. They fed them special, high-vitamin diets. They reserved their best food for the dispensary, while the officers and the men ate spam until their faces turned green at the mention of the word. Somehow they managed to keep the personnel in far better condition than the equipment.

They knew that, before the air-strip was finished, the Japs would probably try to bomb them heavily. They knew that sound tactics called for such a bombing—to destroy their work before they could get their planes in and a fighter cover overhead. And they knew that without such a fighter cover— with only their own guns and the planes from Guadalcanal to protect them—they probably would have to build a lot of the air field all over again. But every last man in the outfit lived for the day when the strip would be finally finished. Until that day arrived, they were quite content to drive themselves and to be driven, as long as they could see the long stretch of runway getting a little longer with every sunset.

I spent a week with Commander Goodman watching him at his almost hopeless task of running a health farm on a jungle island. It wasn't exciting medicine nor even particularly interesting. But it was important medicine, quite as important as any surgery in the front lines.

Nights, when the rains came harder than ever, I used to sit in Goodman's steaming hut, typing away at my notes while he and his visitors wrote letters home by the one dim light. Goodman always had many visitors. They came to participate in a strange ceremony—the nightly picking of the paper. Promptly at eight o'clock every evening, Jerry Goodman would go over to a shelf piled high with newspapers. These arrived every few weeks in a great bundle, sent by his wife from Baltimore. Each night, Goodman would reach into the pile and pick out a newspaper at random. The rest of the officers would sit around anxiously waiting. Sometimes the paper would be three months old. Sometimes it would be full of spot news, aged by less than six weeks in transit. But whatever it turned out to be they would all solemnly wait until Goodman finished the first reading, which was his by right of ownership. Then the paper would pass from hand-to-hand and every man would read his fill of the news right down to the local society items. You got the feeling, listening to them, that some of those officers—from San Francisco and New Orleans, from Milwaukee and Denver—knew more about Baltimore than they did about their own home towns.

After everyone had finished with the paper it was passed on to Goodman's favorite corpsman. In return for opening and closing the hut's shutters this boy earned the right to take the paper back to his tent every night and to lord it over *his* buddies.

Off in another section of the island was the advance echelon of a marine air group—the men who were waiting to operate the air field. While they waited they were by no means idle. They built their own camp, and it was a beauty. They set up all the complex operations equipment of the air field. And they made preparations for the much larger influx of men which would come when the building of the field was more advanced.

These marines—like all the others I have seen—are the most democratic outfits I have ever known. Their officers allow themselves few if any special privileges. They take a surprising degree of interest in the welfare of their men. It showed itself in many things. But most of all you saw it in their hospitals. For nothing was too good for the marines' hospital. Their doctors—Navy men assigned with Navy corpsmen to service with the Marine Corps—could ask for almost anything with the certainty that, somehow or other, the marines would provide it as long as it was for the good of the hospital. The attitude went a long way towards explaining the marines' terrific *esprit de corps*. I think it also explains in a large measure why the marines' doctors seem to be the finest, the most hard-working and the most effective I have seen anywhere, in the States or abroad. If I tell about one of them in particular, I hope all the others I have met will understand. Because Lieutenant Commander Nesburn was typical, in many ways, of all Marine doctors.

Dr. Nesburn had *drive*, plenty of it. And with drive— and not too much else—he had built and run one of the best little hospitals in the South Pacific. I still ache all over when

I recall the day I made the rounds with him, for it started at sun-up and it didn't end until sixteen hectic hours later, hours in which he managed to do the work of three men while I trailed him like the tail on a comet.

Perhaps I appreciated Dr. Nesburn all the more because of the surroundings in which I found him. For all I could see, when I got there in the dawn, was a shambles of a camp, set deep in the Russell's mud and seemingly ready, soon, to sink out of sight.

My jeep broke down five hundred yards from camp and I sloshed my way through the gumbo, past a maze of un-opened crates, un-erected huts, oil-barrel showers and rain-soaked, floorless tents. The rain, still dripping off the coco-nut palms, was already turning to misty steam in the rising heat of the sun as I made my way up the slope past a screened-in mess tent and a jumble of mud-mired trucks, wondering as I walked why on earth I had ever listened to the doctors down South who had told me to look up Nesburn's place.

Then, topping a small rise, I came upon the first real buildings I had seen in miles, a cluster of barrel-shaped tin huts.

They stood on a little hillside, where the rows of coconut palms ended and the jungle began. The tiny wards were set on coconut-log pilings, so that they jutted out from the slope and overhung the jungle. A rope barrier had kept the madcap jeep drivers from churning the hospital grounds into mud. Except for the red clay around the foxholes, the ground was covered with a patchy green grass, the nearest approach to a lawn I had seen north of New Zealand. Below, along the edge of the jungle, a brook sparkled and tinkled over a coral dam.

It wouldn't have looked like much back in the big bases down South, where Navy sick bays have all the fancy fittings

of the best hospitals in the States. But against the background
of dreary desolation I had just passed through, the little
dispensary seemed a beautiful oasis of coolness and cleanli-
ness.

I found Dr. Nesburn perched on top of one of the huts,
wrestling a balky tin ventilator into place with the aid of
four corpsmen and much hammering. I couldn't tell who
was who, so I just stood there and yelled, "Hey, commander." Presently, one of the five bees detached himself from
the swarm and waved to me. Then, with a slide and a leap,
he was off the curving tin roof and grasping my hand, all
in one motion.

Lieutenant Commander Nesburn was a short man, quite
stocky and with an energetic manner that should have warned
me of what I was in for. He started to question me about
half a dozen things at once. Had I had breakfast? Had I
really seen the big hospitals in New Zealand? How was
Guadalcanal coming along? Did I have much trouble finding
the place? And what on earth did I expect to see and write
about among his little shacks?

Before I could begin to answer, he looked at his watch
and whistled, "Whee-e, I'm late for sick call." Then he
rushed me, like a broken-field runner, past the foxholes to
a canvas shelter, where about a dozen boys had lined up,
waiting for him. He put down his hammer and washed his
hands, sponging them with alcohol. Then he began to ex-
amine the men, keeping up a pair of running conversations—
with me as well as with the patients—all the while.

The men in line were typical marines; very young, tall
mostly, thin, cocky in a way and obviously proud of themselves. But incredibly polite. A few of them looked over at
me when the doctor questioned them and remembered to
say "Sir" when they answered. But most of them managed

to call him "Doc" with a friendliness and familiarity that carried with it no element of disrespect.

Their troubles were, mostly, minor ones; a bandage to be redressed or a cut finger or a Cactus Crut. But one lad complained of a pain in his groin and the doctor, who a minute before had been burbling along with a stream of queries for me and jokes for his patients, became serious. His fingers felt along the lad's stomach and down towards the soft spot near his right hipbone. His manner changed, became more serious, and he took his time. He turned at last toward a corpsman and whispered something. Then he told the worried lad he'd better spend a day or so in bed.

To me he said, "It might be too much chow. But it might be appendicitis. We'll put him under watch for a few hours and see how he comes along." Then the next boy came forward and again he was joking as he re-splinted a broken finger.

The last of the men were examined and dismissed by eight o'clock and we stepped out to make a round of the wards. We hadn't gone far before a youngster came up and stopped Nesburn. "Say, Doc," he said. "We can't seem to make your jig-saw puzzle work out right."

We followed the boy off to where a new hut was in process of erection. In a few seconds I had lost Nesburn. He wriggled under the foundation piling and disappeared. The young marine followed him and also vanished. I waited, then knelt and peered, but all I could see was daylight coming through under the far end of the hut and illuminating a large hollow under the building. I stood up and dusted myself off, just in time to see the doctor and his guide coming out of the hut's open doorway. They noticed my astonished stare and Nesburn began to explain.

"We're trying out a new twist in foxholes," he told me. "With the wards built on a slope like this, we've got plenty of head-room underneath. So we shore the sides up with coconut logs and an earth bank. And on top we've got both a floor and a ceiling, to break the fall of anything coming down."

"But what has all that got to do with the Houdini act?" I queried, still puzzled.

"Oh, that's simple. We shinnied up through our patented escape hatch. See, we've cut out a section of the flooring and hinged it, just like a trap-door. Then we're going to balance it with a counterweight and hold it with a latchbolt. The next time Jap bombers come overhead, we won't have to run our stretcher cases out through the rain in the dark. We'll just slip back the bolt, drop the door and slide them through the hatch. We figure we can empty a full ward in less than two minutes this way."

"That is," he finished, "if the damn thing works."

Nesburn caught my smile and added, with a grin, "I used to be an ophthalmologist back in Los Angeles. But when they survey me out of this outfit, I'll be a cross between a half-baked architect and a construction engineer. The funny thing is, I'm getting a great kick out of it."

We started toward the wards again but two corpsmen stopped us with a dispute over the last remaining bit of wire screening. Nesburn borrowed King Solomon's solution for that one and split the wire between them. Another lad came up with a roll of blueprints. And all three of us dropped to the ground and pawed over the plans until the difficulty was settled. I began to despair of seeing any medicine but in the end we reached the wards, taking our shoes off at the door like Mohammedans at mosque. It was nine-thirty.

Inside, the white-walled room was lined with two rows of cots, each spaced out by a bedside table which, on closer examination, proved to be a packing crate on legs. At the far end of the structure, where it overhung the ravine, an extension had been screened off as a sun porch. Here fully half of the patients were seated or sprawled on the deck, reading or playing cards. A radio was shut off as we entered and all the men came in and stood, approximately at attention, at their beds, while the doctor made a quick turn down the line and examined their charts.

Then he called out, "At ease," and they returned to whatever they had been doing, while we started going over the cases, one by one.

One boy, a carbureter mechanic, had been burned by 100-octane gasoline. He lay on his side, so that the bandages running all up his right leg and arm gave him the grotesque look of a well-bound mummy. One expected to find, underneath these swathes, a mass of raw, distorted flesh. But instead, when Nesburn's speeding fingers had gently lanced the bandages into a myriad of tiny strips, one saw the skin of a new-born babe, fresh, pink and hairless, with only a few—a very few—spots where any grafting might yet prove necessary.

For a time, the doctor and I were both so intent upon studying the success of his treatment, that we did not notice what was happening behind us. Then someone said, "Stop pushing," and we turned to find the entire wardful of patients examining the restored skin over our shoulders.

The momentary silence was broken by a deep, throaty voice from the rear of the crowd, a voice from a bearded non-com, older than the rest, with cauliflower ears and the broken nose of a small-time prize fighter. "Oh, boy," it boomed. "Oh, boy, Doc, if you'd only wrap *my* face in bandages for a while."

Before we turned to his next patient, Nesburn showed me the case record. The diagnosis read, "Anxiety neurosis" and the record told a story of increasing tension over a period of weeks, starting when the Russells had first been bombed, shortly after our landings there. The boy had finally turned up at sick-call after more than a week without any sleep at all. The final entry, dated two days before, read, "Barbiturates, as required."

I expected to see a haggard, shaking wreck. The boy we found was thin, perhaps a bit sallow under his deep sunburn but smiling as he stood there and with bright eyes. Nesburn asked him whether he had had a good night.

"Gosh, Doc," he answered, "I thought they had surveyed that kind of sleep!"

We kept working down the line, past the six malaria cases, the four dengues and the five or six plain colds. To each, Nesburn gave only a few minutes but there was nothing cursory about his speed. He knew most of the boys by name. But whether or not he knew the name, he always seemed to know the case without reference to the records. And whenever the patient had a complaint, of any sort, the interval at the bed lengthened, the record was reread and the doctor probed more deeply.

It was nearly twelve when we finally reached the man who had been sent to the wards during the morning sick call. His pain was more clearly localized now, about four inches above the right groin. Nesburn palpated the tender region repeatedly, as if reluctant to decide. Then he turned to the corpsman and said, "Three o'clock. Better get him ready. And tell them we'll use a spinal."

We left the wards in silence and walked back to the outpatient shelter. A weapons car, half auto, half truck, had drawn up and we climbed in. Already seated there were three youngsters, fully dressed and sweating in the hot sun. All of them had the emaciated look of malaria cases, with a yellowish cast of eyes and skin that comes from long dosing

with atabrin. But they seeemed a happy if incongruous looking lot, their helmets over their shoulders, their long green
trousers tucked into their buckskin marine boots and their
feet perched on jam-packed sea bags. The doctor explained
that they were on their way out, to one of the non-tropical
bases to the South.

"That's the only reward for getting malaria," he said, "if
you get it often enough and bad enough, you can bid this
tropic paradise good-by."

As we jounced over the miles of rutted roads that led
through the endless aisles of palms to the PT Base, the three
marines kept waving good-by to every last sinkhole and
gulley. Only when the trees parted for a moment and we
drove across the half-completed air-strip, the strip their outfit was waiting to operate, did they turn silent, as silent as
Nesburn had been ever since we left the hospital.

After we had cleared our charges with the evacuation
officers and were lurching our way back home, the doctor
spoke at last. "There's a tie-in between those kids and our
neurosis case. I wonder if you noticed it. Those boys we
just sent out *thought they were glad* to be going South.
But they weren't really, not in the sense of getting away
from the fight. Our neurotic isn't a coward either. But there's
a tension on these islands that gets a lot of men. Sometimes
I think it's worse than actually fighting.

"You see," he continued, "we came out here to run an
airfield. That's what our outfit is trained to do. We left our
pilots back on the Canal, but we thought we'd have them up
here, sixty miles nearer to Rabaul, in a few days or so.
Instead, we've been stymied by the rain for weeks. We're
sitting ducks here, waiting for the Nips to attack us. And
we can't hit back.

"That's why I didn't send Old Sleepless out with the
rest of these kids. Because we're almost set now. That boy

is going to be all right if I baby him along a little for another week or two. Because after that, we'll have our planes in and he'll be busy like the rest of us, dishing it out instead of taking it."

The talking seemed to loosen him up, as if an idea, half understood, had been troubling him and now, at last, had become clear. He seemed again as unworried as he had been when I met him in the morning. He began to fill in the background of their story for me, telling how they had set out from the States under sealed orders, uncertain where they were going. "I've still got my Aleutian undies packed in my sea-chest," he explained, looking wryly at the sweat stains on his thin, open shirt.

He told me, too, of their landing in the Russells and how the colonel had insisted on getting the hospital set up even before the rest of their gear came off the barges. He had thought the Old Man a nervous nellie then, but when the bombings brought their casualties and then the heat prostrations and the malaria cases cropped up, he changed his mind about the colonel.

We were still talking when we drew up to the little dispensary again and realized that it was three o'clock and too late for lunch and time to operate, anyway.

On our way to the operating room, we passed the hut where I had first found Nesburn in the morning. Once again he disappeared. I began to suspect another trap-door until his voice sang out overhead, "Just a minute, Maisel, be right with you. Got an idea for this damn ventilator." He hammered and heaved and then, as quickly as he had left me, he was back and we continued on the double.

As we ran, Nesburn said, "Don't let me forget the colonel. Got to fix up his ankle again."

The operating room was at the end of a long hut which

also housed the records room, the laboratory, and the dentist's office. The corpsmen were all ready for us when we stepped in and began to wash up, going through all the motions made famous by Dr. Kildare without any of the fancy equipment he always used for a backdrop. Yet, though our sterilizers were converted pressure cookers and our sinks were made out of worked-over gasoline drums, we followed the standard surgical routines quite as rigorously and came out quite as aseptic as if we had been back at the Los Angeles County Hospital.

Stepping sideways, so as not to touch the washroom door, we entered the operating room. The patient was already on the table, hunched over on his side. A corpsman handed the doctor a hypodermic and he began the intricate, precise procedure of administering a spinal anaesthetic. The boy on the table winced only once, when the needle first pierced the skin. Then the local anaesthetic deadened all pain and he didn't even know when the second needle entered the spinal canal.

In a moment, the corpsmen had turned him onto his back and arranged their sheets and towels so that only a six-inch square on the lad's abdomen lay exposed. The doctor took up his scalpel, measured the distances with his spread fingers, found his point of incision and cut. The room grew quiet except for the sharp regular slap of metal against rubber as the corpsmen passed the doctor his instruments.

The taut, fatless flesh parted quickly, exposing the muscle barrier. Then it, too, was open and the peritoneal cavity exposed. The doctor peered through the small opening, while the corpsmen drew it wider with their retractors. His tan rubber-clad fingers reached in and found the appendix. The corpsmen, watching Nesburn's eyes above the white mask, relaxed. The appendix wasn't ruptured.

The room was getting hotter as our breathing worked over

the stale air. The roving corpsman came over and wiped the doctor's brow with a sponge.

In a moment he had the suture in place and the little bag of poison out. Before throwing it into the waste can, a corpsman held it high with a forceps, so that even the patient could see it. The boy, who until then had been clenching his fingers behind his head, as if still anticipating the beginning of the operation, looked at the amorphous sac just once. Then he closed his eyes. The fingers relaxed and he breathed easily.

The operation continued but the strain was gone from the room. I remember noticing little things I'd missed before. The contrast between the almost dainty white gowns the corpsmen wore and the big, sneaker-covered feet that poked out below the hemlines. And the funny way their bare legs and shoulders showed through when they moved and the backs of the gowns parted, for none of us wore more than shorts underneath.

Then Nesburn finished the final suturing, the roving corpsman checked over the sponges and swabs and the patient was trundled out of the room. Through the open door, the steamy outside air came in like a refreshing breeze. The corpsmen removed their gowns and we all relaxed and sat in the doorway and smoked our cigarettes. One of the boys went off and came back with some sandwiches. I suddenly realized that this was our first food since early morning. My watch showed five-twenty.

The phone rang and Nesburn went inside. A corpsman said, "Bet ten to one it's the colonel again, yelling for his cast to come off." Then Nesburn came bounding out saying, "Let's get going or we'll never reach the Old Man."

We put our shirts back on again and I followed the doctor over to the canvas shelter for evening sick call. The admit-

ting corpsman called them "the usual bunch of skibbage":
a few cuts, one heat prostration, one malaria relapse.

But one lad came in on a stretcher, stiff and unconscious.
Nesburn examined him from head to toe, but there were
no marks, anywhere on his body. As the doctor worked over
him, the boy began to come to, sitting up finally and holding
his head in his hands.

The circle of his friends, who had been gaping in awe all
through the examination, now relaxed. They grinned and
winked and the standing corpsmen took up the grinning.

"Another member?" the doctor asked.

And the boys answered, "Yep, Coco-Head Number
Three."

Nesburn examined his patient's head again. Finally, after
much searching, he found a small bruise. He taped the spot
and a corpsman brought up an ice-pack, while the rest of the
men stood around kidding the victim and I gazed on it all,
dumbfounded.

Then Nesburn turned to me and explained, "Coconut concussion. They stand under a tree. Zowie. A six-pound coconut hits them on the head. Then they become members of
a new club, The Russell Island Coco-Heads. We've had
three cases so far. They're all knocked cold but they all come
to, not much the worse except for a headache. We keep them
under observation for a few days, just to play safe."

It was quite dark as we finished with the remaining patients
and started a final turn through the wards. The night corpsmen were coming on duty and Nesburn gave them their
orders as we made our way past the cots. A few radios were
turned on and the wardboys were bringing in trays for the
bed-patients. The ambulatory patients drifted over to the
hospital mess tent.

But we weren't yet done with our day. We left the wards

and entered the small office, where Nesburn and the records clerk settled down to clear up their paper work. He dictated his write-ups directly to the typewriter while I sat down at last and began to tally up the score of the day's work.

It was nearly nine o'clock, fifteen full hours since I had first met the doctor working on that tin roof. In that time he had treated twenty-eight out-patients and forty-two in the wards. He had performed one appendectomy, dressed fourteen other wounds, diagnosed three malaria cases and two dengues. He had discharged six men back to duty and made a twelve-mile run to the PT Base. And, in between time, he had helped with the erection of the two new huts and settled a scrap over some screening and fixed that ventilator and called the colonel's tent a few times to find how the Old Man's broken ankle was feeling.

Now, with his glasses on, signing papers, he looked tired for the first time. But he shook it off and bounced up again, when the paper work was finished. We went back to the wards for a last look at the appendix case. The kid was sleeping quietly, his hands still held behind his head, just as they had been on the operating table. We left a corpsman beside his cot, nose buried in a murder mystery, and headed for the muddy road that led past the mess tent into officers' country. It started raining just as we reached the colonel's tent at the end of the line. We drew back the flaps and went inside.

The colonel, a man of fifty, was propped up in bed, his leg held high by a rope which led from his splint to the tent's ridgepole. Two other officers were seated between the bed and the paper-covered table. Nesburn introduced me and we shook hands all around. Then he turned to the colonel's leg and the Old Man leaned over, addressing himself to me in a bellowing voice that no one could have failed to hear.

"Listen, son," he said. "If you're going to write up this pill-pusher, tell the truth. Tell them he's a fiend. He keeps me tied on this gallows of his just so he can watch me suffer. He keeps ordering me around. Says I can't walk. Says lie down. Says stay in bed. Don't do this. Don't do that. I'm supposed to be running this outfit. But I'm not . . . he is, the conspiring little sawbones."

Nesburn tugged a little harder than necessary at the leg and one of the other officers nudged me, while the colonel continued to hurl imprecations at the smiling doctor. When the cast was rearranged and the rope rehung for the night, Nesburn doused the hanging light, leaving only a small lamp burning at the head of the Old Man's bed. The other officers said good night and walked out with the doctor. I was about to follow when the colonel added a last word.

"Good boy, that Nesburn. A couple of years with the marines and we'll make a real medic out of him yet."

Then he winked.

Outside, Nesburn looked at his watch. "It's only ten to ten," he said, "and we've finished the whole routine. Let's rustle up some supper and you can tell me about the real hospitals down South."

We started off through the rain, but the phone rang in the colonel's tent and then his voice, bellowing through the canvas, stopped us. "Hey, Doc," he yelled. "It's Doctor Furguson, from the A.A.'s. Needs you to help him set a fracture."

CHAPTER VII

FIGHTING SHIPS AND FIGHTING DOCTORS

IT may seem strange to the reader that so much of a book about naval medicine should be concerned with everything but the doctors on the combat ships. For on the sea, if anywhere, must be the romance and excitement of naval medicine—the life-saving heroics which make a good story.

Yet, if we stop to think of the Navy as it exists today, we realize that a great part of its medical effort *must* be concerned with the shore establishment—the men who man the bases scattered all over the earth, the men who fly the land-based patrols, the marines who fight on land and the SeaBees whose somewhat different fighting is also done on shore. From this shore-based Navy arises a very substantial proportion—perhaps even a majority—of all naval casualties.

Fighting ships, of course, do produce spectacular casualties. But any given ship may go through many months—sometimes through a whole war—without a single battle injury. Assignment to such a ship may mean, for the naval surgeon, an endless round of preparation for the casualties that never come, interrupted only by routine physical examinations, inoculations, and the treatment of minor ills and injuries such as he would be just as likely to meet on any street in a Middle-Western town.

Even after the battle, a great deal of the medical work takes place on shore. Injured ships, whether they have won the victory or tasted defeat, must make for their base to repair their own wounds and to bring their critical casualties to a hospital ship or shore hospital. Thus possibly 90 per cent of all Navy medical practice, we discover on analysis, does not take place on the combat ships.

Yet destroyer and cruiser and battleship medicine can be intensely exciting. The practice of medicine on a combat vessel demands special skills and traits of character which only a few doctors can be expected to possess. More than for any other medical posts, the Navy is doubly careful in selecting its personnel for the fighting ships. Most of the combat doctors at sea are selected from the younger and more vigorous of the regular Navy physicians. The older regulars —men like Alanson Bryan, Lucius Johnson, Joel White, John Robbins, and John E. Porter—are usually assigned to supervisory and administrative positions. They run the large naval hospitals, at home and abroad; jobs for which they are supremely well qualified by their long acquaintance with Navy methods and their intimate knowledge of Navy ways.

Many of the reserve doctors who have entered active service since the war must likewise be used to man the shore hospitals. These men are often specialists who can achieve their fullest usefulness only when working at their specialties in collaboration with other specialists. Older men—be they regulars or reserves—are also less able to stand the strain of combat. Many of them consider themselves fully vigorous and in the prime of life. But in most cases the Navy would be taking an unjustifiable risk in placing a man well past middle-age at a sea-going post where other lives would depend solely on his stamina and physical resistance in a time of long-continued crisis.

Thus most of the senior medical posts on board the combat ships fall to men who have had some years of peacetime naval experience. These men are young enough to go right along with their crews through rough weather, long weeks at sea and the final strain of battle. They know their Navy inside and out. For they are naval officers quite as much as physicians.

Typical of these regulars is Lieutenant Commander Joseph A. Syslo. He has seen his vessel, the great new battleship, *South Dakota,* through the battles of Santa Cruz and Guadalcanal. In both of these struggles the ship was hit and many casualties were suffered. But his own battle began long before the ship met the enemy.

For many months after they put to sea, Syslo studied and altered the organization of his department. He planned the distribution of his medical equipment and his personnel with all the care and ingenuity of a strategist plotting a battle. Here is his description of the meticulously planned set-up that existed just before the ship entered action:

With the exception of one battle dressing station and a few first-aid stations, the medical department is so located that it has armor above, in front, behind, and on its left and right sides. When battle is imminent, all doors and hatches are closed and approximately one-half of the medical department personnel is below armor. Personnel and matériel are so distributed throughout the ship that first aid can be administered anywhere from the shaft alleys—in its bottoms—to the twelfth level of the superstructure. Moreover, if during battle, one or even two parts of the ship are so severely damaged that medical supplies and personnel are destroyed, the distribution is so planned that the remaining part of the ship has sufficient medical facilities to carry out even major surgical procedures.

On the third deck, below armor, there are two battle dressing stations: the forward one consists of the entire peacetime sick bay area, medical storerooms, a thirty-six-bed sick bay, surgical dressing room, operating room, scrub room, dispensary, laboratory, record office, doctors' office, dental office, isolation ward, and air-conditioning unit; the other is located aft of the machinery spaces in a living compartment having approximately 180 beds and one medical storeroom. This space is provided with a portable operating table, an electric sterilizer, and all essential items for performing emergency major surgery. A third battle dressing station is located on the main deck, just aft of the wardroom which is used as a collecting station and in the immediate vicinity of a berthing space containing approximately two hundred beds. This dressing station, too, is so equipped that major surgical procedures can be carried out with relative ease.

In addition to these stations, there are two first-aid posts, one on the seventh level above the main deck forward, and one on the third level above the main deck aft. These are supplied with all first-aid materials except those necessary for performing major surgery. On the second deck, there are two more small first-aid stations. Here, a small amount of first-aid material is kept to provide emergency treatment for a relatively small group of men whose battle stations are on the second deck. On the main deck, forward and aft, in the immediate vicinity of good shower facilities, there are two gas-decontamination stations which, in the absence of a chemical attack, function as first-aid stations.

Medical supplies are further dispersed in 140 first-aid boxes containing battle dressings, bandages, cotton, tourniquets, powdered sulfanilamide, and morphine Syrettes. Five portable battle lockers contain dressings, bandages, cotton, splints, emergency surgical instruments, blood plasma, morphine, sulfonamides, etc. These are used to convey treatment to casualties who for one reason or another cannot be brought to a collecting station. Gun bags, consisting largely of cotton, bandages, and adhesive tape are provided for all machine-gun mounts.

Morphine Syrettes are widely distributed. Every commissioned, warrant, and chief petty officer is given a box of five Syrettes. They are also placed in varying quantities in all first-aid boxes, portable battle lockers, hospital corps pouches, first-aid and battle dressing stations. Every box of Syrettes is numbered, and around the narrow edge of each box are placed six strips of adhesive tape, ten inches long and one half inch wide. One of these is strapped around the wrist or ankle of a casualty to indicate that he has received a full dose of morphine.

Such painstaking and detailed planning, preparation, and training is essential on every combat vessel if its medical department is to meet the sharp, compelling, unpredictable emergencies of battle. On the *South Dakota* the crisis came on October 26, 1942, off the Santa Cruz Islands, a few hundred miles east of Guadalcanal. From over the horizon— seemingly from every direction—came squadron after squadron of Japanese dive-bombers and torpedo bombers. One after another they struck at the battleship. But evasive steering and an anti-aircraft umbrella drove them off. All but one of the enemy was forced to turn away or was brought down before its bombs could strike home.

But the last bomber made it, dropping a five-hundred-pound missile which struck a forward turret. Bomb fragments scattered over the main deck and the first superstructure. A senior officer on the bridge—four levels above the main deck—was hit and seriously wounded. On the main deck itself forty-nine of the crew were injured. Then all firing ceased. The enemy planes were driven off. And the work of the doctors began.

Immediately one of the changes, which Commander Syslo had introduced, paid off. In the original plans of the ship no provision had been made for a main deck battle dressing station. But Syslo and his associates, in the months before the battle, had foreseen the need for such a station. When the bomb struck, it was there, ready for work.

The administration of first aid went on rapidly. At the same time the doctors made a preliminary classification of the injured. Those requiring the most urgent treatment were moved first to the sick bay, while the corpsmen still worked on the others at the dressing station. Months before, every man in the crew had been immunized against tetanus. But the Navy takes no chances. Every injured man received a booster injection of tetanus toxoid. Sulfathiazole tablets were administered to everyone. Again Syslo was taking no chances with infection.

One officer was brought in with a perforating wound of the neck which had severed his jugular vein and thyroid artery. He was bleeding profusely, yet the doctors saved his life by a prompt tying up of the severed vessels. There were few other hemorrhages, for although many wounds were extensive and serious, they were seared and coagulated by the very heat of the flying bomb fragments. Such wounds, fortunately, did not bleed at all.

Ten of the fifty injured men had compound fractures. These were splinted temporarily and then operated upon as soon as the most serious cases of hemorrhage or of abdominal injury had cleared the operating tables.

Meanwhile, as the doctors worked, the ship headed for port. Yet so successful was their surgery, so complete were their facilities and so thorough their preparations that only eleven of the fifty casualties had to be sent on to a hospital ship. The rest remained on board while the battleship put out to sea again to rejoin its task force.

Three weeks later, on November 15, 1942, Syslo's ship participated in the great night battle with Japanese warships off Guadalcanal. This was a far more severe action. The fight took place just after midnight—for thirty-five eerie minutes the great vessels traded blows.

Almost at the start a number of Jap shells found the ship and caused casualties. This time the doctors had to work in blackout, for the superstructure of the ship had been per-forated, prohibiting the use of white light above the main deck. To add to their difficulties, a fire main was ruptured on one of the upper levels of the superstructure. Cascades of water flooded the rooms below to a depth of eight inches, forcing upon the corpsmen the added task of re-rescuing wounded men who had already been placed on the decks of these rooms. Some casualties occurred as far up as the twelfth level of the battered superstructure. Here rescue parties were forced to bring the injured down in rope slings and canvas stretchers, for the interior ladders had been shot away.

During the night no attempt was made to isolate the dead. Injured and dead alike were brought down to the various hospital quarters and treatment was given to all who still lived.

By morning, a census of casualties had been completed, disclosing five officers and thirty enlisted men killed during the action. Eighty-five others were injured, of whom five died within twelve hours despite intensive treatment. But of the remainder—including twenty-two serious cases—every man was saved.

On the largest ships, such as Syslo's, the senior medical officer and as many of the others as possible are selected from among the Navy-wise regulars. But in a rapidly expanding Navy there are simply not enough of these regulars to go around. They have been pulled from shore positions; replaced by reserves wherever they could be replaced. And still, time after time, the Navy has had to place reserves— civilian doctors in uniform—on combat ships.

Repeatedly the reserves have worked out wonderfully well. Most of them have studied the Navy's correspondence courses while still in civilian practice. Many of them have spent peacetime vacations cruising and training with the Navy. Once they enter the service they receive intensive indoctrination and refresher courses ashore. Then, from among the younger reserves, the most skillful, the most widely experienced and the temperamentally and physically best qualified are selected for assignment to the ships. On all the larger ships they work under the guidance of experienced regulars. Today the once sharply defined dividing line between the *reserve* and the *regular* at sea, is becoming increasingly obscured. If the war lasts another year, the distinction will have disappeared entirely, except as a matter of Navy record.

Typical of many of these reserves was one I met in the New Hebrides. If I tell his story in some length, it is because I know it intimately and not because it differs in characteristics or degree from many another tale of the civilian doctors who now fight at sea. As I see it, the important thing about the story of Dr. Coates is not that he was different. Such importance as it may have lies precisely in the fact that Coates was typical of hundreds of physicians—the fish-out-of-water who have fitted in.

For months before our troops invaded the Central and Northern Solomons, the Navy kept hammering at the Jap concentrations there in what, by a triumph of understatement, has become known as a "softening-up" process. Much of the job fell to a cruiser task force which, repeatedly, slipped out of its newly built bases, raced the long leagues northward and then—usually about midnight—threw its hundreds of tons of shells into some selected Japanese coastal bivouac.

It was on one of the last of these missions that Lieutenant Elmer T. Coates first saw action with the Navy. A transport had brought him out from the States only a week before, as green a novice as ever walked a deck.

The first time I met Dr. Coates, he seemed filled with that homesickness that no one ever really gets over in the South Pacific. He looked so utterly lost I asked him to come with us, up to the big new hospital and later to the officers' club. Maybe it was because I was homesick too or maybe because I was a good listener, but Dr. Coates seemed to hang onto me all that afternoon and evening. He talked mostly about home, about his childhood and his years at the University of Nebraska, and about the girl he married and the office he opened in San Antonio. He showed me the pictures of his two beautiful children and that gave me an opening to show my own worn photographs of my daughter.

But most of all he talked about medicine, about how he had always wanted to specialize and how he had begun to get somewhere as a baby doctor, until the war came. Then he went to the Navy; to Corpus Christi for a few weeks and then to the sleek, powerful cruiser we could see anchored out in the bay. It wasn't exciting talk. I remember wondering how on earth anyone came to send this big, soft, homesick kid to fill a surgeon's post on a tough cruiser.

But in the week that followed, the week before his first battle, Dr. Coates learned much. His senior surgeon, old-timer Commander Cliff Storey saw to that. Together they explored the ship until every last emergency kit, from the fantail hangar to the for'ard magazines, was firmly positioned in the young doctor's mind. He mentally blueprinted the location of every last bandage in the sick bay storeroom, of every instrument and needle in the combination office and operating room.

And yet, all he learned in those few days only made him the more aware of how little he knew. As the task force jockeyed for position and settled down to the long, fast, zigzag daylight run for the Solomons, Coates felt himself the only man on board that cruiser who didn't have a job to do. He toured the ship with Storey, but it wasn't his ship. He watched the gunners in the turrets, as they checked their breeches and cleaned the guns and polished spots that weren't really there. And he found himself envying those boys who were already veterans; envying especially their part in all that was going on. Cliff Storey must have sensed Coates' thoughts, for he sent him on another round of first-aid cabinet inspections, just to give him something to do.

All that day and evening, while the rest of the ship went purposefully about the business of preparing for battle, Coates found himself a passenger, an onlooker watching a drama about to unfold rather than an actor in it. When night came, they had passed San Cristobal and started up the slot that runs the length of the Solomon chain. At ten, as they slipped past Guadalcanal, general quarters was sounded and Dr. Coates went up to his battle station on Control Two.

This was in the aft control tower where, as junior surgeon, he was supposed to stay as a sort of reserve, in case the main control station with Dr. Storey in it was shot away. There were some fifteen men there and, at first, he still stood off alone, not wanting to get in the way. But about eleven something happened, one of those minor things that sometimes occur on ships to draw people closer. This time it was a rainbow, one of those incredible moonbows that spring up on dark nights in the always rainy South Pacific. It started about three points off the fantail and worked up until they had a complete arc in the sky, faint and phosphorescent. The weather-wise sailors discussed it, as they stood waiting, considered it and weighed it as an omen, and tossed the idea around and chewed it over just to have something to talk about that wasn't about what was coming next. Before he knew it, the doctor was in conversation and telling about something like this he'd once seen back home in Texas. And after that, he was one of them and the time passed faster.

By midnight they were almost there. Away off to port they could make out a low, long island, Santa Isabel. To starboard and nearer their channel, was New Georgia, black and silent and ominous. And ahead, across Kula Gulf, was the great, round extinct volcano that is Kolumbangara. At twelve-fifty they made their turn and started to move into the Gulf, an eight by twelve mile stretch of water as black, at that moment, as Tojo's heart.

The Japs must have sensed that we were around. They opened up their searchlights; not just a single light but seven or eight.

That was all our ships needed. Before Coates quite knew what was happening, the destroyer screen that had been feeling the way, found the road lit up for it. Five-inchers started firing all over the place and the Jap lights went out, one by one. They didn't dim out, the way a searchlight does when you flip the rheostat. They went out the hard way . . . boom . . . as the shells hit all round them. In less than a minute the night was black again, but now we knew just where the Jap was and just how worried he was, too.

Over the phones, Coates heard a voice. "It looks like a nice night," it said. "There's a fine crowd here."

Then came the first salvo from the big guns and novice Coates thought the ship had been hit. He'd never before felt the way the deck stings your soles and sends waves of air billowing up your pants legs when a cruiser lets go with all fifteen of its big guns at once. The glare blinded him and the recoil threw him against the bulkhead. But the voices on the phone were calm and, more important, they were still there. By the time the second salvo went out, ten seconds later, he had a grip on himself. For one thing, he knew he was on the sending end, for the moment at least, because he could see the shells as they left the guns, arching over the water in threes, like great balls of fire, and bursting among the coconut trees along the shore.

He was excited, so excited that he missed the turn that marked the end of their first run, missed it entirely and stood there wondering whether it was ever going to end. He counted the salvos and, that way, he knew how much time had passed. But he kept thinking there was something wrong, because thirty salvos meant five minutes and they had been scheduled to turn off on a new course in four. When he reached forty-eight in his counting, he looked back for the wake and saw its phosphorescence shear off to the left. That meant they had made the second run on schedule and were going into the third leg, the leg that would take them out of the Gulf. That was when he felt his breath go out and realized he'd been holding it all the time, while he counted each earsplitting burst and waited for the turn.

Just as he was beginning to relax, the ship shuddered with a new rhythm, different and more terrible than the beat of outgoing shells. There was a long second of silence, while each man looked at his neighbor in the control tower with eyes that said, "We've been hit." Then the voice came back on the intercom. It was damage control saying, "Blowback in Number Three turret." Another voice said, "Fire in the magazine." And another, not on the phone this time, but beside him, said, "Here's where we swim."

There was a long pause, during which the last of the scheduled salvos came from the six-inchers all along the line. Then the voice came in again, calmer now, saying, "Fire under control; fire in Number Three under control. Dr. Coates, report to the wardroom; Dr. Coates, report to the wardroom to tend casualties."

The sound of his own name coming over that phone brought him back to earth. He didn't know what he was going down to, but one thing was certain. That voice on the intercom was telling him to go to work. He was a passenger no longer.

He took off the phones, put them back in the rack and started down the ladder. One of the men, he never know who, patted him on the back and said, "Go to it, Doc."

✦

Below he found the wounded, laid out all over the sick bay and overflowing onto the broad tables in the wardroom and the floor of the admiral's cabin and even the passageways. He couldn't hear their pain, because they wouldn't let it out between their tight-clenched lips. But he could see it on their faces and read it in their eyes. And so he knew, without thinking it out, that the first thing to do was to treat the pain and leave their burns till later.

He started from where he stood and worked across the sixty-foot wardroom, developing a rhythm as he went. *Feel along the arm. Left hand into pocket. Up comes a morphine syrette. Bite off the head because your hands are holding the arm just right. It's not the way the book says you should do it, but it's quicker. Then press till the first drop oozes out of the needle. Then slow down. Careful now as you shoot the Heaven-sent stuff into the muscle. Drop the empty tube on the floor. Now the crayon to the man's forehead, if he has a forehead that isn't burned crisp. Or to his chest or his leg or wherever there's skin that can be marked so he won't be given a second dose he couldn't stand, by someone else. Then move on to the next man. And don't look at the far wall. You'll know when you get across the room, but it seems to take forever.*

Then, halfway across the deck, he found his hand reaching for an arm that already had another hand on it. He looked up and saw Cliff Storey, doing the same thing and concentrating just as hard and therefore just as surprised to meet him. And they would have both laughed, only somehow you couldn't laugh in a room full of desperately injured men.

They turned then to the plasma and Coates began to understand why Dr. Storey had been hoarding those plasma packages and "borrowing" them and begging them and trading for them at every stop from Panama to the South Pacific.

Because they were way above their quota on plasma, five times above their quota. Yet now they could use every last precious bottle.

So, while the corpsmen cut away what was left of the men's clothes, they sweated and worked in the hot wardroom, fighting their way through the burn-toughened flesh with the thick plasma needles and pumping life back into men who should, long since, have died. And watching them not die, because plasma is wonderful stuff if you have it. Thanks to Storey, they had it, plenty of it.

Time passed and the morning came. But Coates didn't know it because he didn't eat breakfast and he didn't see the sun. He kept on fighting death down there in the wardroom, doing the things he had to do and marveling at the guts of the men before him who should have groaned but didn't.

While he fought, he knew though no one told him, that the men topside were fighting another battle up there. He knew just how it would be; how the Jap would send in his squads of torpedo bombers to try to kill the ships he couldn't touch when they had walked right up the line the night before. Coates knew it by things he wouldn't have understood a week before . . . by the way the deck tilted when the ship took a turn, by the way the needle in his hand shook when the guns chattered overhead and by the way the bubbles churned up in the plasma bottles that hung all around the room.

Then it was all over up above. The guns went quiet again, and in the stillness, the men who lay on the tables below could hear a cheer that sifted down through the battened hatches and rang through the very metal of the hull. They didn't know the details; how our planes from Henderson Field had let the Japs come on until the task force was in sight and then pounced upon them from the clouds. They didn't know that the score stood seventeen Japs down and two probables against three of our own planes lost and two of our pilots safe.

They didn't know these details down below. But they heard the cheering and, from then on, the fight in the wardroom took on a new note. It was still a steady routine; morphine, plasma, cleaning the burns, applying cod liver oil ointments, dressing the wounded with vaseline gauze. Dawn came and noon and night. Time passed only in terms of bandages applied and, most of all, of bubbles rising slowly in the plasma bottles as the fluid dripped life into the men's veins. It passed in small units to some men. And in huge, shapeless lumps of work on boys like Gunners' Mate Crewson whose burned out body drank up the plasma and cried for more until they could hardly find a vein in which to place their needles. On the second day, when the clocks were again in focus and they were streaking ever nearer to port, it took both doctors and two corpsmen an hour and a half of work to get a needle into place. But it was worth it, for Crewson came out of coma that time, stayed out and joined the growing list of sure survivors.

It was then that Coates first noticed the squooshing sound that followed him around. He brushed it off and tried to shake it away, as if it were some ringing in his ears. But still, every time he moved, it came again, "Squoosh-squoosh-squoosh." He began to be afraid to hear it, afraid to ask anyone else if they heard, afraid it was a noise that sounded only in his head. He worked on, pretending to ignore the noise, until a corpsman tapped his arm. "Take your shoes off, Doctor," the kid said. "They're full of sweat and splashing."

He kicked them off his swollen feet and, after that, the sweat worked onto the floor. He tightened his belt another notch and didn't know it was because he had lost ten pounds between the heat and the sixty hours since he last had slept.

He made the rounds once again and then, at last, Coates

and Storey sat down and tallied up their score. Five men had never lived to reach the wardroom. Twelve had been carried out, one by one. But around them there were twenty who would definitely pull through. And twelve more who'd make it, if they lived through the next few hours.

Those twelve were the men who had been nearest the gun that had exploded. When the breech that should have closed had failed and the shell that should have hit the Japs had hurled its flame instead backwards into the turret, these were the men who caught the full force of the flames. Their faces and arms and chests were burned, yet in that they differed little from those who were recovering already. But deep inside their lungs they carried other, more fearful wounds, the injuries of burning gases that had leaped down their throats as if to strike at their very hearts.

Such inner wounds cannot be treated by oils and pastes and bandages. The Navy's experts prescribe supportive treatments, the very plasma treatments they had already given these men to ward off shock and renew the body's will to fight. And these were obviously not enough.

As they watched these boys—Cavanaugh and Dunn, Gregory, Outlaw, Pruitt, and Crowley, little McGarry and tall George Meuth—it seemed as if there was nothing more they could do for them. Within their blasted lungs, nature was throwing up its own defenses, trying in its own way to tip the scales against death. But therein lay their greatest danger. For, as the injured tissues sloughed off their waste matter, the swollen throats of all twelve began to fill with bloody fluid, throwing them into racking spasms of hopeless coughing, spasms that would only hasten death unless stopped quickly.

Then it was that Coates fell back upon his baby-doctor training. Somehow his tired mind reached back, out of his new world of racing ships, into the old life he had quite forgotten in the last two days of fighting. He recalled an old country doctor's trick for fighting diphtheria, where nature too gets confused and kills in its attempt to save. He knew it wasn't the modern technique, but he told Storey about it nonetheless. And, almost in desperation, they decided to try it.

Acting with speed now, once the decision had been made, they cut lengths of fine rubber tubing from off the exhausted plasma bottles. The corpsmen gathered around Coates while he slipped a tube down deep into one man's gasping throat. They saw him bend over and suck slowly, gently, upon the protruding rubber cylinder. Then, as a corpsman held up a pan, Coates expelled from his own mouth the bloody fluid he had drawn from the sick boy's chest.

The corpsmen looked at Storey and his eyes said, "Go ahead." The group dispersed and each man found his patient. Gently they worked, imitating each motion Coates had made, draining away the wastes, while the room grew quiet and even the other wounded watched. Then, one by one, they stood erect, their job done, their patients breathing freely again.

From then on, all hands concentrated upon the twelve. Their pulses were felt every fifteen minutes. Their plasma bottles were rigged so that the flow never stopped, so that the new bottles began to give their first drops before the old ones had quite yielded their last. They looked for things to do for those boys, they yearned for things to do. And yet, for all they did, they found themselves standing most of the time, just watching.

As they kept their vigil, a sailor came through and began to open the dogged-down porthole covers. The light that was the second dawn streamed in across the tables of the wardroom. Through the portholes Coates saw the distant, lush green of tropic hills. He went to the nearest porthole and put his head out. The clean wind filled his lungs as he pressed his shoulders against the steel bulkhead and craned his neck. Ahead, far off but getting bigger, loomed the great white hull of the hospital ship, its red cross blazing in the brilliant sun of morning.

He turned towards Dr. Storey and, together, the two veterans went off to write up the records for the thirty-two who lived.

Coates and Storey brought the twelve most seriously injured survivors over to the *Relief* where their work was taken up by Dan McCarthy and Ed Denneen, by Tom Garvey and Lyman Hoyt. In the end, two of the twelve succumbed. But none among the doctors of the *Relief* were surprised. Their astonishment was reserved rather for the fact that any of these seared and mangled wraiths pulled through.

Late that night I went down into the quiet wards with Commander McCarthy. Swathed in their bandages, the burned men looked ghostly in the dim light. Most of them were asleep and we left them undisturbed, each watched over by a corpsman who sat beside the bed, tensely conscious of his responsibilities.

Chief Bo's'n's Mate Henry Dunn was under an oxygen tent and we would have passed his bed like the rest. But he saw us in the dim light and waved his hand weakly towards his mouth to indicate that he wanted to talk. For a moment the doctor hesitated. Then, concluding that the strain of talking would weigh less on the man than the feeling of having been passed by, the Commander lifted a flap of the tent and we both bent down to catch Dunn's words.

His voice was low and incredibly hoarse but his phrases came out clear and coherent. He told us how he had been outside the hatch, "on the topside patrol." After the explosion he had not known that he was injured. He had rushed over to grasp a fire hose. It was only when he lifted the hose and watched it drop from his hands, that he realized that his palms were both burned to the bone. Now, talking to us, he was troubled by a terrible sense of guilt. Somehow, he thought, his failure to get that hose into the burning turret had caused the death of some of the men within.

The doctor listened quietly. Then slowly he explained the thing to Dunn—explained that a water stream sent into that red-hot turret would only have parboiled the already injured men. Dunn listened, his face immobile. We could hardly be sure that he heard the words or knew their meaning.

The doctor repeated the whole short explanation over again. And this time Dunn responded, at first not with his mouth but with his eyes. After a while he moved his lips and the low hoarse voice said, "Thanks, Doc, I hope you're right."

He closed his eyes and we turned down the flap of the oxygen tent. Outside, on deck, McCarthy stopped for a smoke. The night air resensitized our nostrils and we smelled again the acrid powder odors that still hung around the men —nearly two days after the explosion. I asked the doctor about Dunn's chances and he shrugged his shoulders. We were silent for a while again. I suggested coffee. Again McCarthy shrugged his shoulders.

Then he said, "You drink it, Maisel. I'll meet you later in the wardroom. I want to take another look at that boy."

I watched my old friend's tired back as he walked slowly towards the ladder that led to Ward M. Somehow I knew then that it would be a long time, perhaps sunrise, before McCarthy came up for coffee. He was going to watch that boy until he pulled him through.

CHAPTER VIII

THE OTHER WAR IN THE PACIFIC

IN San Diego, before the battalion sailed, the doctors had given the men lectures about tropical diseases. Those who thought of the tropics in picture postcard terms promptly concluded that they were going to be sent to retake Java and Borneo at least—if not the Philippines. Others, who remembered the lectures of the preceding week—"How To Live Off the Land In the Far North"—concluded that it all didn't mean a thing; for all anyone could tell they'd probably break the outfit up and put them to training new cadres.

But the battalion remained intact. When they went out on the transports and the doctors repeated lectures on living in the tropics, Alaska at least was ruled out of their long list of possible destinations. The men gathered in clusters around the wall maps and began to discover how countless were the islands in the Pacific, how many were their possible destinations. It all made for lots of conversation.

Sergeant Eddie Simpson picked Tonga-Tabu as their first port of call. Not that he knew any more than the others, but the name of the place appealed to him—it sounded like the kind of tropics he had always heard about. Eddie gained a lot of prestige with the outfit when it turned out he was right.

The doctors lost prestige at the same time. They had been warning the men about malaria half-way across the Pacific. But at Tonga-Tabu no one had ever heard of the disease. Then the order came to break camp again. This time the doctors didn't merely lecture the men about malaria. They handed out pills, small half-circles of some yellow medicine that they told the men they'd have to take every day as a "prophylactic."

The marines put the pills on their tongues and made wry faces at the bitter taste. Most of them swallowed and forgot about it. But Eddie Simpson was the sort of boy who had never liked medicines. He couldn't see any sense in taking bitter pills when there was nothing wrong with him. On the second morning, he palmed his pill and pitched it over the side after chow. The third day out he even had a bit of fun, dropping the pill into Johnny Mulholland's scrambled eggs and watching the wry face Johnny made when he bit on the thing.

On the fourth day they landed at Guadalcanal—a quieter place now than it had been a month or two before, when the fighting was still going on. The men would have liked to have gone up into the hills and hunted out a few Japs—just for practice. But as things turned out, they didn't even get as far as Henderson Field. For four days they worked from sunup to sundown, unloading their heavy gear from the great transports, getting it over the side into their landing barges and ducks and then transferring it again onto the beach and up into the coconut groves, where it formed great piles around the trees. There was an awful lot of equipment, more than anyone had ever realized before; guns and ammunition, case after case of small arms, cots and tentage and building materials, pipes and generators and sawmills and endless cases of food.

Eddie Simpson drove one of the amphibious ducks and, that first day, he thought he liked the place. The mountains looked nice as you came in across the water. When you ran up on the beach and saw all the equipment they had there, it made you feel strong and secure. It was hotter than at

Tonga and the minute you came away from the water the mosquitoes began biting you, particularly towards nightfall. But except for that and the cold chow, Guadalcanal wasn't half as bad as they'd painted it.

That night, Eddie slept in the coconut groves under a pup tent. He slept soundly after the day's work—except when the little lizards began to crawl around and he had to brush them off. Mosquitoes didn't bother him much, particularly after he learned to keep his sleeves rolled down and to tuck his trouser cuffs into his boots. That left only his face and hands for them to bite on.

Some of the other boys weren't so lucky; they seemed to attract mosquitoes. Some made the mistake of sleeping stripped, only to find themselves covered with welts the size of quarters. By the second night, everyone had a hearty respect for the mosquitoes. They began to make jokes about them, saying that "these Guadalcanal mosquitoes were so particular they lifted up your dog-tag to see what kind of blood you had before they would condescend to bite you."

By the fourth day the whole outfit was dog tired. The rains had come and they were drenched right round the clock. Men thought themselves lucky when their turn came to work in the ship's steaming hold, because that meant they would eat decent food from the galleys. On the beach everything was gooey by the time they got a chance to eat it. Most of the men threw the slop away and tried to live on chocolate bars. In the end they were all glad when they got the stuff off the beach again and loaded onto small boats and motor-powered lighters.

That fourth night, when they left Koli Point behind and headed up the coast, the exhausted men lay under the stars and enjoyed the relative coolness of the sea trip. They didn't know where they were going. Some were scared and all were excited. But at least they were glad to be leaving Guadal-canal.

Eddie Simpson had his first premonition of trouble late that night. It wouldn't be right to say that he felt sick, but his head hurt a little and there was a curious dull ache in his bones. He was tired, dog tired. But then who wouldn't be tired, he thought, after the four days of work they had just been through?

Towards morning he became chilly and huddled down be-neath a tarpaulin. None of the other men seemed to notice how cold it was getting. Eddie remembered later thinking that that was a little bit queer.

But in the morning, when they made their landing at the new island, Sergeant Simpson was on the job with the others. And it wasn't until six days later—after they had put up their tents well inland and built the screened-in mess halls, and got the dispensary set up and manned their gun posts—that Eddie began to feel sick again. By this time he had developed a hearty respect for the mosquito. He was as careful as any-one else to arrange his mosquito-bar netting over his cot at night. And he never went around after sundown without rolling down his sleeves and closing the cuffs—no matter how hot it was.

When the real chills came he thought of malaria and he found himself regretting that he hadn't taken all the little yellow pills that had been given to him. But then he remem-bered that the doctor had said there was no malaria on this new island and he shook off his weakness and went to work, that seventh day, along with the rest of the men.

It wasn't until nearly noon that he became really sick. He felt his face flushing and his head ached as if a band were being tightened around it. His mouth was dry and bitter. Even in the rain, his skin felt dry. Then he vomited and a couple of his buddies lifted him into a jeep and took him to the dispensary.

By the time the corpsmen had shifted him to a cot, the first chill had come on. They took his temperature and said it was 104°. But Eddie couldn't understand that because he felt cold, bitterly cold. His teeth chattered no matter how tightly he tried to clench them. And he shivered despite the five blankets that covered him.

Then the chill broke and he began to sweat. His clothes were soaked and even the blankets felt damp, and he stretched out and slept a little. He felt better again—tired, but better—and he threw the blankets off and tried to get up. But his knees shook and he didn't resist when the corpsmen pushed him back onto the cot and covered him with all the blankets once again.

The doctor spent a lot of time on Eddie that afternoon, feeling under his ribs where something had swollen and seemed to press on his stomach. He made Eddie take the yellow pills—not just the small, half-round pill but three of the large ones, full size. Then he took a little gadget that pricked the tip of Eddie Simpson's third finger and he smeared the little drop of blood on to a glass slide and went away.

In half an hour he was back with the bad news. Eddie Simpson had malaria—the first case on the island.

There have been thousands of Eddie Simpsons in the Pacific. Some got malaria because, like Eddie, they were just a bit too cocksure and careless. Others took their suppressive drugs and still got malaria—for although our drugs work well, they do not work invariably. A few of the men who got the disease, in the early days of our occupation, paid for the mistakes—the natural, honest, inevitable mistakes—of their officers and doctors. For very few of our naval and marine and army officers who were sent to the South Pacific Islands had ever before worked in the tropics. And the New Hebrides, the Solomons, and New Guinea are among the most malarial areas on earth.

The problems of dealing with malaria in the Pacific Islands differ in many ways from those faced by the physicians in the malarial areas of our southern states. For one thing no one who has not spent time in the steaming, swampy jungles of these desolate islands can fully appreciate the conditions under which anti-malarial campaigns must be carried on. The climate works against man and for the mosquito in innumerable ways.

The men—engaged as they are either in building bases, fortifications and defenses or in combat against the Japanese— must ignore many of the simple lessons of living which both the natives and the whites in the tropics have long since learned to follow. The siesta, an honored institution which calls for the cessation of all work from eleven in the morning until two-thirty in the afternoon, goes by the board when lives depend upon constant activity, unceasing building and continuous watchfulness. The ordinary rules—to live as dryly as possible, to keep out of the swamps, to build one's house on piles—all these are observed mainly in the breach. The all-important rules that proscribe staying indoors from sundown to sunup must, of course, be ignored.

Instead, the necessities of life and of fighting seem to demand that man do those very things which will place him most fully at the mosquitoes' mercy. He fights in the wet and the muck where the mosquitoes are thickest. He debilitates himself by long hours of exertion, by eating catch-as-catch-can, and by the constant necessity for interrupting his sleep either to fight or to secure shelter from air raids. Even in the rearward areas, where time and security have permitted the building of screened huts and the utilization of individual nettings on bed rolls and cots—even there an air raid or the danger of one will cause the personnel of an entire island to throw itself into water-soaked holes in the ground. These may provide protection from falling missiles, but they inevitably lay the men open to attack from the Japs' great ally, the mosquito.

In our southern states the *Anopheles* mosquito is known as a night flyer. It hides by day and one can enter the densest swamps with relative safety as long as the sun is up. But in the tropic jungles, *Anopheles punctulatus,* the principal carrier of malaria, flies and attacks right round the clock. The dank wilderness in which it lives is perpetually shrouded in semi-darkness and the hours of daylight provide little if any added security for men who must expose themselves.

In the swamp lands of Georgia or Louisiana one can also be certain that only a limited proportion of all the mosquitoes will carry the infection. The seasonal change in climate tends to kill off old crops of mosquitoes and to produce new hosts of *Anopheles.* Each new seasonal swarm must secure its infection from human carriers before it can spread the disease to other human beings. And such carriers—even in our most malarial regions—seldom constitute the vast majority of the population.

In the Solomons, on the contrary, virtually every native is infected with malaria. One doctor whom I met in the Russell Islands showed me his charts recording the examination of fifty-two local natives. Thirty-eight of the fifty-two showed the enlarged spleens characteristic of the malaria victim. Twenty-eight of the fifty-two showed parasites in their blood. Of the fourteen whose spleens were not enlarged, nine were parasite positive. Thus forty-eight out of fifty-two, in a single test, showed themselves to be malaria carriers! In the opinion of the doctor, an experienced malariologist, "The rest also harbored the parasite, but happened—at the moment—not to show up positive on the first test."

To add to the problem, the Japanese succeeded in "seeding" most of the areas in which we have fought. One would have expected that Japanese medicine would have been fully prepared to cope with malaria on a large scale in the Solomons, for the Japs had had much experience with the disease in China, in Formosa and elsewhere. Yet in Guadalcanal the vast majority of their troops were infected with malaria and suffered from it perhaps even more extensively than did our own troops. By the time they were driven off the island they had succeeded in raising the degree of infection of the mosquito population to a new high level. Thus, our troops were forced to fight, simultaneously, against two enemies. Statistically—in terms of men incapacitated for further fighting—the *Anopheles* mosquito caused fully as many casualties on Guadalcanal as did the Japanese.

The very nature of the malaria cycle presented special difficulties for our medical forces. The disease itself is caused by a tiny parasite, a plasmodium. These parasites are obtained from a victim of malaria by any one of a number of varieties of *Anopheles* mosquitoes, who will suck up infected blood upon biting the carrier. Within the mosquito's body most of the parasites—the asexual *schizonts*—will die off. But a few will prove to be *gametocytes*, male and female parasites. These will breed within the insect's stomach. The fertilized female cell will bore into the stomach wall of the happy, buzzing, oblivious mosquito. A cyst will form within the mosquito's body cavity, growing until it matures and bursts. Then, still within the *Anopheles*, it will liberate a swarm of new parasites, millions of them. These find their way into the mosquito's salivary glands. The little dive-bomber is re-armed, ready to strike down another victim and inject him with a new dose of malaria.

Once they get into a man, the new malaria bugs begin to develop in the blood stream. Each parasite bores into a red blood cell, nests comfortably, and proceeds to divide and redivide and redivide again. As these spores grow to their full size, the blood cell is finally ruptured and the new plasmodia go their way through the blood stream, looking for new red cells to conquer and destroy. Thus by repeated cycles, the organisms multiply with extreme rapidity unless something interrupts their growth.

The process of infecting the mosquito—from the time of the first bite to the time of transmission to a new human being—takes about twelve days. The incubation period within the human victim varies from a week or ten days for some forms of the disease to many weeks and sometimes even months. But eventually the cycle is completed within the human blood stream. The parasites burst their blood cell hosts and boys like Eddie Simpson experience their first paroxysm of chills, fever, and sweating.

During this cycle of development the physicians and malariologists have several opportunities to break the vicious circle. They can isolate malaria carriers from the mosquitoes and thus limit the reinfection of the mosquito population. This, however, is extremely difficult to achieve in the tropics where, instead of seasonal swarms of mosquitoes, the climate produces its mosquito population in an endless stream. In the tropics, too, there is great difficulty in isolating the extremely heavily infected native population, the principal human reservoir of malaria.

Once the mosquitoes are infected—as they usually are—the malaria fighters' next hope is to prevent the mosquito from biting man. This, too, he can accomplish with fair measure of success—by denying the mosquito his breeding grounds, by repelling him with noxious substances or by screening off a wall between the human being and the mosquito. But here again the conditions of the tropics, aggravated by the additional difficulties under which fighting troops must operate, make the process of breaking the cycle an extremely difficult one.

A third point of attack lies in the use of suppressive drugs —often improperly called prophylactics. These drugs—quinine and atabrin—cannot prevent infection. But they can keep most infected men from showing the classical symptoms of the disease. The men may carry the malarial parasite within their blood stream, but its growth is arrested and its ability to bring on the chills and fevers of malarial ague is at least temporarily inhibited.

Finally, a fourth point of attack becomes available when infected men are treated with heavier doses of these same drugs and "cured" of both their sickness and the infection. Such treatment not only relieves the victim of the disability induced by malaria but may also serve to render him once again non-infectious.

All of these things we can do and are doing in the tropics to limit and arrest malaria. Each method has its limitations, made all the more apparent by the extra difficulties of carrying on a war at the same time. No one of the methods is 100 per cent effective but, using them in combination, the Navy and its associated forces in the Pacific have succeeded in holding malaria in check, in beating down the sickness rate month by month and in holding the death rate from malaria down to a tiny fraction of 1 per cent!

This victory—and it is a victory quite as great in its scope as any we have yet achieved against the Japanese—is in large measure the accomplishment of a single man, Commander James J. Sapero. For Sapero has been the organizer and the spark plug of a series of Malaria Control Commissions which

now operate in every area in the South Pacific where the infected *Anopheles* and our troops must meet.

In the process of organizing the campaign against malaria,
Sapero has also won another victory, for the organization he
has set up is one of the outstanding examples of the sort of
co-operation between army, navy, and marine forces which
was once thought impossible of achievement. Backed to the
fullest extent by Admiral Halsey (and by Halsey's senior
medical officer, Captain Arthur H. Dearing), Sapero has
managed to build what he himself terms "a bastard force"
of army, navy and marine personnel—doctors, entomologists,
hospital corpsmen, laboratory technicians, engineers, and
"just plain swamp drainers." This force has repeatedly demonstrated the effectiveness of its work to local commanding
officers who in the beginning were quite often extremely skep-
tical of the entire procedure. Today such skepticism has disappeared and every area commander includes the Malaria
Control people in the first echelon of his forces. Their work
is recognized as a military essential quite as important as
adequate anti-aircraft, coast defense, scouting or supply.

It was not always so. In the very beginning a few mistakes were made. Some sites were picked for camps and air
fields in which hard-pressed military men ruled out the warnings of the Malaria Control people. They spoke of these
sites as being dictated by "military" necessity. But they soon
learned that any equation of military necessity must include,
as an essential factor, the local conditions of malaria infection and mosquito breeding. The best air field site in the
world, they discovered, will prove of little avail if half the
troops who must man and defend the air field are incapacitated by disease.

For a long time, however—since those first few early mistakes—Commander Sapero and his subordinates have had
what amounts to the unique authority to give orders to offi-

cers of far higher rank than they themselves carried. This authority has stemmed directly from Admiral Halsey and has been backed up to the fullest extent. Today, when the head of a Malaria Control unit—he might be a young navy lieutenant, or a marine, or army captain—points out the "military necessity" of avoiding this or that malarial site, his words are given great weight by the military authority and he is overruled, if at all, only when every other consideration weighs against it.

Before Malaria Control was organized on a basis encompassing the entire South Pacific Command, much effective work was done by small local control commissions, set up on the several islands we then occupied. But despite this early work, the necessity was soon appreciated for the setting up of a large organization which could shift its men from area to area as the need arose and which could bring substantial forces to bear upon any given area both to carry out its own mosquito elimination projects and to train local troops for a continuation of the work.

Commander Sapero's first two units were sent out by plane from the States. But even before they arrived Sapero began finding his personnel among the various fleet units and in the Marine and Army groups. Among the hospital corpsmen in the Navy, in particular, he found many a man who had had previous experience in insect control—in Panama, or China, or Samoa, or in the States. Often these men had been assigned to positions which did not utilize their skills. Sapero was permitted in such cases to secure the reassignment and transfer of these men.

There was, for example, Pharmacist's Mate Bernard Sheridan who had been doing routine administrative work in Samoa. Sapero found him in an office there when he first passed through. He remembered that Sheridan had lectured on parasitology some years before the war at the Navy Medical School in Washington. And so the commander "acquired" Sheridan, taking him with him as he went on to the Fijis and the Hebrides. I found him in the latter islands where he had already established an enviable record for himself in training other men for the work.

Another such find was Pharmacist's Mate 1-Cl Dener K. Lawless. He too had had years of experience in the great parasitology laboratory of the Navy Medical center in Washington. But when Sapero found him he was doing routine work on an aircraft carrier.

With such men as a nucleus, Dr. Sapero began to build his units, splitting them and re-splitting them as they grew, so as to take on additional areas of work. The doctor himself flitted around the islands, dropping in unexpectedly on his various units and conducting surveys of new areas for the Command. Of all the much traveled men in the South Pacific, I believe Sapero was the hardest to pin down to one spot. When I was in New Caledonia, he had just left for New Zealand. I missed him by two days at Auckland and returned to New Caledonia only to find that he had left an hour or so before. I would have missed him again at Espiritu Santo but for the fact that weather grounded his plane. And so, after weeks of chasing the man, I finally found him— a tall, sunburned, smiling person dressed in old khaki trousers and a skivvy shirt, seated on the narrow shelf which passed for the porch of his laboratory hut. His feet were bare, but he held one shoe tightly between his knees while he prodded at it with the point of a bayonet, in a vain attempt to break off at least the outer layers of mud.

He greeted me with a wide and friendly smile, motioned me to a perch on the same narrow board and then—noting the mud on my own boots—picked up a second bayonet and offered it to me. Then he wiped the sweat from his dripping forehead and went back to work while I started to dig at my boots and we both talked.

Sapero was quite willing to talk. He was one of those facile, fluent characters to whom words came readily, with colorful sweeps of phrase that brought an image standing up before your eyes. But his talk was mostly of others—of the way Admiral Halsey and Captain Dearing made his job easy for him or of the way in which "a little son-of-a-bitch in whom I had no faith at all" was sent into some Godforsaken swamp and proceeded to drain it "as dry as Kansas." Most of what I was to learn about Sapero himself I had to find out from others, from his subordinates who had a tendency to worship him as if he were really some strange God who swooped out of the skies every now and then to cheer them up and bring them new equipment and help them win their arguments with the local generalissimos.

Part of their worship for Sapero no doubt arose from the fact that he operated a sort of personalized air-mail service. Many of his units were shifted around from spot to spot with such rapidity, as the need for their services grew, that they would never have received any mail at all from home if Sapero had not managed to pick it up here or there in his travels and then come bringing it in, in great batches, on his inspection trips.

The commander was an old navy man, a "regular" long before the war. But, possibly because his units were all mixed ones, neither he nor his men seemed to have any particular consciousness about rank. You got the feeling, as you saw him work and as you heard others talk of him, that he had left his stripes back in San Francisco and that the job that they were all performing was essentially a civilian operation. Yet I doubt if he ever had a disciplinary problem and I know that he had an application list, of men who wished to join his units, long enough to fill a small filing cabinet. For though the work was dirty and often unappreciated, Sapero had succeeded in making it exciting and interesting.

The doctor explained to me the basic outlines of the work, the way in which his units first surveyed an area, identified the strains of mosquitoes inhabiting it, charted the swamps and streams and then selected sites which were marked "taboo" and sites which were marked "ideal." He told me of how they had developed improvised equipment (even before their real apparatus had arrived from the States) for spraying swampy areas with oil and for instituting drainage wherever possible. But most of all he talked of the individuals in his units, of men like Leo Terzian up at Tulagi and Captain Downs in the Russells and Colonel Parks on Guadalcanal.

Until I had met the man I had found the entire picture of the malaria problem a confused one. Everyone—doctors, corpsmen, and naval officers—was ready to talk about it. But everyone had his own ideas and all the ideas seemed to run counter to all the others. But by the time Dr. Sapero had finished with me—when his boots were clean and his bag was repacked and he hopped into his jeep to make another try at the air field—he had managed to whip all the divergent opinions I had heard before into a single simple clearcut whole, the picture of a problem which had no one solution, no magic cure—but a problem which was nonetheless being rapidly solved by a war of attrition.

This, I think, is Sapero's greatest accomplishment. The men in the Pacific, most of whom have never heard of the smiling young doctor, owe much to this man because of his ability to reduce a seemingly complex problem to its relatively simple essentials and because of the companion ability, which few men possess, to assemble and train and inspire a mixed group of men who would go out and apply his simple miracles all over the South Pacific islands.

✦

I first saw his units at work on the little island of Tulagi to which he had sent two young lieutenants, James Richard Kingston and Levon A. Terzian. Kingston had studied medicine at the University of Minnesota and then gone on for post-graduate work at Harvard, returning to Minnesota for private practice and then for years as a public health worker in the northern part of that state. Terzian, a doctor of science rather than a physician, had taken his Bachelor's and Master's degrees at the University of Pennsylvania and then studied at Johns Hopkins, where he specialized in protozoology. A thin, wiry young man of only thirty-four, he had already made a reputation for himself, before entering the Navy, with his research in malaria at Johns Hopkins and his work on peritonitis and shock at the Foundation for Clinical and Surgical Research at Philadelphia.

At Tulagi, however, both young doctors had shelved for the duration the dignity and seriousness one usually associates with research workers. They were engaged in a strenuous—and to them exceedingly exciting—battle against *their* enemy, the mosquito. They threw everything they had into the work. But it would be wrong to speak of it as a grim battle; there was nothing grim about these youngsters. They pitched into the swamps and waded hip-deep in the muck and shinnied up the coconut palms to catch mosquitoes and lay down in the road ruts to watch the larvae as if it were all good, clean fun. Terzian even managed to have a good time catching dengue, a disease which makes most men feel like minor martyrs. Together with their fellow mavericks, the young lieutenants who ran the little Tulagi naval dispensary, Terzian and Kingston had formed the Tulagi County Medical Society, an organization which will hardly achieve a place in medical history, but which will certainly be long remembered in the Solomons for the antic quality of its meetings.

They needed humor on Tulagi—plenty of it—for when they got there early in January of 1943, that little capitol of the Solomons was one of the worst malarial spots in the South Pacific. For personnel they had only themselves and two or three corpsmen, "tall boys" (as Terzian described them) "whose heads would show above the reeds." They also had one tent, one microscope, and one typewriter. Their initial poverty had its advantages however, for it permitted the Control Commission to select its new equipment with great care. Most of the new equipment belonged to others and it can hardly be said that the original owners co-operated in Terzian's selection. But by hook or by crook they soon acquired one jeep and the part-time use of another. On these vehicles they mounted homemade sprayers, assembled out of the debris of wrecked equipment which was left on the island after the marines had finished with it. And they began to give Tulagi the most thorough going-over any South Pacific island had ever received.

At first the going was extremely hard. Most of the personnel on the island were engaged either in anti-aircraft defense or in building roads and encampments—for the place was in a transition period; it had ceased to be a battle ground but had not yet quite gotten to the point where it could be considered an established rear base. As Terzian and Kingston and their corpsmen started to work over the island, the construction troops on the roads fell into the habit of kidding them. They were called "swamp ducks" and "clam diggers" and "muck-rakers." Caterpillar operators began to find fun in carefully running a load of dirt into one of their drainage trenches. And their requests that pails and buckets be turned face downward and road ruts be filled in so that mosquitoes would not find new breeding places near camp sites—such requests were considered as just the laughable peculiarities of these strange creatures, who couldn't be any too bright or they would stay out of the swamps in the first place.

Terzian finally converted the island to malaria control. It was a conversion accomplished by unorthodox and unethical means. But it was effective in the extreme. A Marine unit which had been brought in from Samoa had been found to have a few among its numbers lightly infected with filariasis, the disease which, in its later and more malignant stages, brings on elephantiasis with its monstrous swelling of the thighs and groin and scrotum. Filariasis, of course, bears no relation to malaria except in so far as it is mosquito borne. But Terzian began to carefully spread the word that he had found among his mosquito samples a few of the variety *Aedes varigatus*—the vector of filariasis.

When the rumor had had a chance to sink in, the plotters went a step further. They prepared and mimeographed a small illustrated leaflet which depicted—with ample exaggeration—a victim of elephantiasis. The text read:

> IF YOU WANT TO GO HOME
> LOOKING LIKE THIS
> (Picture of elephantoid soldier)
> DON'T SWAT THIS JAP ALLY
> (Picture of slant-eyed mosquito)

Below in smaller type were simple instructions for the destruction of mosquito breeding places, instructions which would apply with equal accuracy to *Anopheles punctulatus* and to *Aedes varigatus*.

One dark night, when the posters were finished and the plotters were still smarting under the sneers of the road builders, a delegation made the rounds of the island. In the morning, on mess hall walls and in front of wash basins, on the outhouses which stand on little piers out in the water all around Tulagi, on fence posts and gun mounts, on tree stumps and the dash boards of jeeps—all over the island the posters were to be found. And around them gathered little groups of awe-struck men for whom malaria held no terror but who still highly prized their genitalia.

Then the panic began. By twos and threes and then by whole platoons—or at least so the story has it—the road crews made for the swamps. By mid-morning the suspected doctors and corpsmen, their eyes all innocence, were explaining things to the island's commandant. And while he thundered imprecations upon them and demanded that they order his road crews back on to the roads, he too was smiling. When the doctors left—still protesting their innocence—they had been promised additional squads of anti-malarial workers and seventy natives to carry on the drainage projects. Months later, one would have been hard put to find on all of Tulagi a single pool of stagnant water.

While antics such as these were effective, most of the work on Tulagi was a matter of constant digging, of sweat and labor and then more sweat and more labor. Many of the smaller swamps were drained completely by running long trenches down to the sea and building ingenious wooden spearheads at the seaward ends of each trench to prevent the sand from sealing up the new ditches with each incoming tide. The less accessible inland swamps, which would have required major engineering operations for their clearance, were oiled regularly. Each unit on the island selected its own malaria-control workers who journeyed down to Terzian's laboratory—which had grown from a tent to a well-equipped hut and from one microscope to three. Here the Bethesda trained corpsmen taught the men how to prepare blood smears, how to identify the malarial parasites, how to trap mosquitoes and how to plan camp sanitation and drainage operations.

By early May, malaria—which had reached almost epidemic proportions in January—had receded well into the background as a menace. Dengue, another mosquito borne disease, dropped off as a by-product of the work. The real test of the success of malaria control came in the great Jap raids of March 6 and 7. During those night raids the majority of the men on the island were forced to take to the foxholes. Then if ever the mosquitoes should have had their innings. Yet no epidemic, nor even any significant increase in the number of cases, manifested itself at this time.

While I was on Tulagi, malaria had not been completely eliminated. Men were in the hospital with the disease and others were being evacuated after they had had one or more relapse attacks of the disease. But these victims of malaria almost invariably fell into two groups. Either they were men who had recently been shifted from Guadalcanal or some other region in which they had originally been infected by a mosquito or they were those who had been on the island long enough to have suffered their first attack in the days before malaria control had gotten fully under way.

The improvement which had brought a lowered incidence of new malaria cases did not, however, mean an end of control work. Terzian took me through his rapidly growing laboratory where he showed me hundreds of malaria mosquitoes, each impaled upon a pin, each carefully tagged and card-indexed to show its species, whether or not it was infected and where it had been found. He showed me his maps of breeding grounds, which indicated with military precision the deployment of the mosquito enemy. Upon these he plotted his enveloping and pincers movements.

In this GHQ of Malaria Control one began fully to appreciate the scope of the battle which had been going on. Most of the *Anopheles* samples came from pools of ground water, from the little stagnant swamps which dotted the jungle. But one variety, about which Terzian was much worried at the moment, proved to be a cosmopolitan breeder. Against all tradition, it seemed to flourish in shallow road ruts and in little pools exposed to sunlight. The presence of this mosquito meant that even oiling and drainage of swamps would not be enough to complete the job of malaria control. There was more work ahead—work which the enthusiastic doctor plotted with all the ingeniousness of an admiral, busy over his maps.

When the Japanese captured Java they took, from the United Nations, control of more than 95 per cent of all the world's quinine. They looked upon this as a master stroke, one which would make it impossible for us to fight our way through the jungles of Burma, Malaya, or the South Pacific islands. For quinine was, until very recently, the only drug which served man in the fight against malaria.

By a curious irony of history the Jap plan miscarried, for only ten years before the war started the Japs' ally, the Germans, had given the world two new anti-malarial drugs. And it is because of these drugs that we are today able to operate on a large scale—and successfully—in areas such as the Solomons. The more important of the two drugs is atabrin, a derivative of the acridine coal-tar dyes. Originally thought of as a substitute for quinine, it is now—in the opinion of many doctors—considered the drug of choice, particularly as a suppressive or control drug.

Throughout the South Pacific wherever men enter a malarial region they take daily doses of atabrin. Usually the dosage consists of a half-tablet per day (about three quarters of a grain) supplemented by a full tablet on Sundays. Suppressive treatment with atabrin usually starts while the men are still on the ships, three or four days from their destination. This serves to build up the level of the drug in the blood stream by the time the men come into direct contact with mosquitoes, a level which can be maintained thereafter by the half-pill treatment.

Atabrin is not unpleasant to take and has not the extreme bitter taste of quinine. It produces few side effects—an occasional slight headache or intestinal irritation—whereas quinine more frequently brings on a ringing of the ears, a temporary deafness or fairly pronounced nausea. It has been found that men with an idiosyncrasy to quinine can take atabrin with impunity. Almost never is a man found with a corresponding idiosyncrasy to atabrin. Finally, the drug is excreted from the body more slowly than quinine. It therefore retains its therapeutic action for a longer time after cessation of treatment. The man who misses an occasional dose of atabrin will remain better protected than one who skips a similar dose of quinine.

Atabrin does have one effect which for a long time frightened many of the men who took the drug. It tends to cause the skin and the eyeballs to become discolored. They take on a yellowish tinge which persists even for a time after the use of the drug has been discontinued. This coloration has, however, been found to have no accompanying ill effects. It eventually disappears after the men leave a malarial region.

The taking of atabrin in prophylactic doses does not prevent infection of the blood stream by the malaria parasite. For this reason the doctors are usually careful to talk of atabrin as a *suppressive* drug rather than as a *prophylactic*. Nor is it completely effective as a suppressive. Some men in any group will tend to show clinical symptoms of malaria—fevers and chills—even though they have taken atabrin faithfully.

The important thing about the drug—the one thing that should never be forgotten—is that these failures are few and far between. Without atabrin entire military units operating in a malarial area could be overcome by the disease within a period of from three to five weeks after the start of operations. In the last war, when we did not have atabrin, this actually happened to entire divisions of the British Army operating in Greece and Macedonia.

With the new drug, however, the commander of a task force can be certain that the vast majority—95 per cent or more—of his men will at all times be free from clinical malaria. Experience has shown that the disease will not break out in epidemic proportions as long as atabrin is carefully and thoroughly administered.

Once a unit is relieved from action, the doctors still have the problem of eliminating the suppressed malarial infections which the men carry in their blood streams. Their first step in attacking these infections involves a determination of the proportion of men who carry the parasites. If this proportion has been held to a low figure—10, 15, or even 25 per cent— the doctors may decide to take all of the men off the suppressive treatment and to provide curative treatment only for those who actually develop clinical malaria when suppression has been discontinued. They can do this in gradual stages, continuing to use suppressive treatment for the majority of the men in order that their hospitals shall not be crammed, all at once, with a vast flood of cases. An examination of blood smears taken from a representative portion of a unit will indicate, with fair accuracy, the proportion of cases which can be expected to develop. Knowing this proportion, the medical officials can govern the rate at which they permit clinical cases to develop after the discontinuance of suppressive treatment—adjusting this rate to the available medical facilities.

Another method, however, is usually favored. This involves the assumption that all men have the disease in suppressed form. Without sending the men into a hospital, they are thereafter given a seven-day clinical treatment with heavy doses of either quinine or atabrin. Those who are not infected are none the worse for this treatment. And those who carry the disease in their blood streams are cured without having suffered the agonies of a malarial attack.

Neither atabrin nor quinine is effective against all of the malarial parasites in the blood stream. Both of them kill the *schizonts,* the asexual parasites which cause the chills and fevers of the disease. But neither atabrin nor quinine is strongly *gametocidal.* A man "cured" with atabrin or quinine may still be capable of infecting a mosquito which can then pass on the disease to scores of other victims.

But here, too, we have a drug, a new synthetic, plasmoquin. Virtually ineffective against the *schizonts,* it is of no use in effecting a cure. But, if given after a cure has been achieved with quinine or atabrin, it has the dual effect of minimizing the risk of relapses and of preventing the further infection of mosquitoes. Plasmoquin is a drug which must be used with great care for it is nearly (but not quite) as poisonous to man as to the malarial parasite. It should not be used simultaneously with atabrin, a procedure which seems to reinforce its poisonous qualities. But when used carefully, in limited doses and under hospital conditions, as a post-curative precaution it is extremely effective.

Some of the doctors in rear-line hospitals have preferred to use quinine for their curative treatments. Others express a preference for atabrin and still others feel that there is little difference in the effectiveness of the two drugs. The general belief is that both quinine and atabrin, when used as suppressives, tend to establish a "tolerance" for the drug in some men. Such patients seem to react more rapidly and favorably when switched from the drug that they have used as a prophylactic to another drug for cure. One of the favorite curative treatments consists of the simultaneous administration of thirty grains of quinine and forty grains of atabrin daily for three days. Since the atabrin blood level builds up slowly, the quinine serves to hold the patient while the atabrin level is being established. On the fourth day the patient is put onto a course of atabrin alone and this is usually maintained until the end of a week.

As the reports of our malarial problems in the Pacific have seeped back to the States, many people have become alarmed by the specter of a post-war invasion of tropical ills. This menace, I believe, has been more apparent to magazine editors than to physicians. Certainly, in respect to malaria, I do not think that it is at all likely that we shall have much reinfestation of our country by returning soldiers or sailors.

It is true that malaria is a subtle disease. Repeatedly men, who have been thought thoroughly cured, have suffered relapses. Sometimes these have occurred several years after the original infection. Some few of the malarial parasites sometimes find a hiding place—in the spleen or in the liver—and emerge years later to reinfect the blood stream. Therein lies the danger, the specter that alarms some people. But if we admit that occasional relapses do occur, several other factors working in the opposite direction must also be recognized.

In the first place, some sections of our country—along the southern Atlantic and Gulf coasts and in some parts of Texas and California—have never been free of malaria. The natives of these regions, particularly when they migrate to our industrial centers, constitute at least as great a danger as will the returning soldiers. They might, in fact, actually present a far greater menace, for we have never succeeded in providing adequate medical treatment for many of these American victims of malaria.

By way of contrast, the men in our armed forces are receiving the finest treatment that the science of medicine affords. The number of those who have died from malaria can be ticked off almost on the fingers of the hands. Men who have developed the disease are not only receiving adequate and thorough medical care during their curative period; they are also carefully watched for long periods afterwards and are never discharged from the services unless every reasonable precaution has been taken to ascertain that the individual is not a malaria carrier. Certainly the few who might sift through this discharge screen unnoticed—if any will at all—will constitute an infinitely smaller menace than our own untreated civilian cases.

But the war has done other things for us. When we entered the war our medical profession had only a few hundred experienced malariologists among its members. Today thousands of doctors—in the South Pacific, in Australia, in China and India, in Italy and the Mediterranean basin—are seeing more of malaria and learning more about it than they ever would have learned in a lifetime of practice in the States. Thus it seems reasonable to expect that any slight increase in the number of malaria carriers within the United States which may occur after the war, will be more than counterbalanced by our infinitely greater and more widely distributed skill in dealing with the disease.

The Navy's work against malaria in the South Pacific constitutes both a military and a medical victory of stupendous proportions. The victory is nonetheless real because we have not entirely eliminated malaria. Enough has already been accomplished to prove that the Japanese hopes of finding an all-powerful ally in malaria have failed dismally of success. With each passing month in the South Pacific our control over the disease becomes more firmly established. We shall still suffer casualties to this disease. In some actions these may still outnumber the wounds of combat. But the second war in the Pacific is being won. The Japs' strongest ally has failed them.

CHAPTER IX

GUADALCANAL

AFTER the war, when old soldiers discuss old battles, there are going to be a lot of disputes about Guadalcanal. Thousands of men will have widely varying ideas as to what things were like upon that bloody island. Curiously enough, all the differing impressions will be right, for Guadalcanal might well serve as a principal example of the dynamic, ever-changing face of war. Over a period of some two months, I entered and left Guadalcanal several times. On each return I found the place so altered as to be almost unrecognizable. Some structures, which I remembered from before, had ceased to exist. In other places, long rows of coconut palms or dense acres of jungle disappeared under the attacks of the caterpillar tractors to be replaced by warehouses, barracks, shops, or hospitals.

Much of the wreckage of battle was already gone in the spring of 1943. Along the beaches, up towards Cape Esperance, one could still see mile after mile of wrecked Jap landing barges and the shell-torn and gutted hulks that had once been proud Japanese merchant vessels, lying now up-tilted on the beach, their superstructures converted into rusting metal lace. In the coconut groves one could still find many a topless tree. But back on Bloody Ridge the jungle was creeping in again, enveloping and burying the scars which men had made and the places where men had died.

Medically, the island had undergone an equal change since the days when Navy doctors accompanied the marines to work in open foxholes and makeshift casualty-stations. Even the doctors themselves had, for the most part, been changed. The veterans of the early battles had been withdrawn with their outfits, to rest and to retrain. In their stead had come new groups of corpsmen and physicians to build new hospitals and to replace makeshifts with the permanent and far more elaborate fittings of a great base.

The tent hospitals which had dotted the island were gradually giving way to a series of small dispensaries. These usually consisted of three or four Quanset huts with fifty to a hundred beds. Most of them had their own operating rooms and many had x-ray equipment.

At some of the larger centers of naval or marine operations, hospitals of 150 and even two hundred beds had been erected. These not only served the men of their own units but provided supplementary services—x-ray and surgical work—for the smaller dispensaries.

Malaria Control had come in and established its stations and laboratories. And, on my last visit to Guadalcanal, Captain Turville had arrived with all the personnel and equipment of a complete Navy Mobile Hospital. Guadalcanal was about to become a great rear base. Today, no doubt, the wounded from far up the line are being brought *into* Henderson Field by the same SCAT planes which once carried them away from the same field in search of medical aid.

As the island changed, so did its medical requirements. The forces on the island doubled and redoubled. But they were no longer living in foxholes and they were suffering less and less from the tropic diseases that particularly seek out men who do not know how to live properly in the tropics. The SCAT evacuation records, even in the early days, bore vivid testimony to the change. In the month of November, 1942, fourteen men had to be taken out of Guadalcanal because of the severity of their fungus infections. By the following February this figure had dropped to zero. So too with a score of other tropic maladies. The island became able to take care of its own. And at the same time, fewer of its men required such care.

But if dysentery and fungus infections were being defeated because the men learned how to live in the jungle and acquired the means which permitted them to live properly, other diseases and other injuries presented their own new problems. Instead of treating gunshot wounds and bomb injuries the surgeons found themselves working—in the quiet periods—upon the fractures of auto accidents and the injuries arising from the heavy construction work that was going on, the building of airfields, piers, roads, and barracks. Medical men turned to treating the attacks of dengue and jaundice. Malaria still filled a sizable number of beds in every dispensary and hospital. And every few days, during all the months between the end of the battle of Guadalcanal and the beginning of the new push at Munda, ships or planes sent the hospitals small groups of battle casualties—sailors injured in a brush with a Japanese destroyer squadron, airmen wounded by the anti-aircraft that futilely defended Raketa Bay or Buin. Despite the changes that occurred continually, neither the doctors nor the surgeons on Guadalcanal had much chance to forget that they were in the military service.

Many of the diseases that affected the men on Guadalcanal—and on all the other tropic islands—were minor ills, insufficient in themselves to justify more than a very few evacuations from the war zone. Yet in the aggregate they presented a tremendous problem to both the military and the medical personnel. Not the least troublesome was dysentery, a disease which can sweep with epidemic force over military units anywhere on earth. On Guadalcanal, in the early days, conditions were such that dysentery spread through many outfits and incapacitated—partly or wholly—large numbers of troops.

Whenever large groups of men enter a tropical area for the first time, gastro-intestinal difficulties are to be expected. The change in climate alone may often bring them on. The eating of tropical fruits, such as the coconut, may likewise cause difficulties. But most of all, such troubles arise from the deterioration of living conditions which inevitably occurs when men are hard-pressed in battle.

The vast majority of the dysenteries experienced on Guadalcanal were of the bacillary variety. Men would first notice the disease as a "belly-ache," often accompanied by a moist and coated tongue and a feeling of intense nausea. Most men were able to continue about their work, although—often enough—the increasing discomfort of stomach and bowels and the accompanying rise in temperature served to effectively cripple a man for several days. Fortunately, one of the sulfa drugs, sulfaguanadine, provides an almost perfect specific against the disease. Using this drug, the victim of bacillary dysentery usually obtains relief from the cramps within twenty-four hours, complete cure in a few days.

Sulfaguanadine is one of the strangest triumphs of chemotherapy. For chemists and doctors actually planned it long before they discovered it. The problem, in treating dysentery, is to find a drug which will fight the germ in the intestinal tract without, at the same time, troubling the patient with numerous annoying and dangerous side effects. The more familiar sulfa drugs—sulfanilamide, sulfathiazole, and sulfadiazene—have been selected from among thousands of the sulfa compounds because they were readily absorbed *from* the intestinal tract and into the blood stream. In treating pneumonia, gonorrhea, or other bacterial infections these drugs were ideal, for they quickly passed from the intestinal tract to the site of the infection—in the blood system, in the lungs, or elsewhere in the body.

But when the doctors wanted to get at the dysentery bacillus these sulfa drugs would not do. They ran away from the intestines instead of concentrating upon them. It was then that the research workers remembered one of their rejects—sulfaguanadine—a drug that was very poorly absorbed from the intestine. They tried it for the treatment of dysentery and its very defects made it work. For with sulfaguanadine a high, bacillus-killing concentration is easily achieved in the intestines while the rest of the system remains virtually unaffected by the drug.

On Guadalcanal the doctors used sulfaguanadine freely. But they did not stop there. For bacillary dysentery is a filth disease which can be prevented by reasonable sanitary procedures. So, all over the island, the doctors left their hospitals and went to the galleys, the mess tents and the latrines to enforce rigid sanitary regulations. They did this while the battles were going on and they did it even more once the island was declared secure. They warred against flies. They supervised garbage removal and incineration. They screened in galleys and mess halls and they threw the fear of God into any man who did not thoroughly cleanse his mess gear.

The troops, once they had had a taste of the ugly discomfiture brought on by the disease, were scrupulously careful in protecting themselves and their comrades. Nothing could so quickly bring on the ostracism of an individual as sloppy habits. The men discovered that much of what they had learned back in the States about field sanitation was not the joke they had once thought it to be. On Guadalcanal they took it seriously and practiced sanitation as an essential routine of daily living. Today, on Guadalcanal, dysentery is rare if it exists at all.

✦

Fungus diseases were a second great annoyance on Guadalcanal, although they too caused few evacuations. One of the worst of these was a ringworm-like infection which made its appearance as a series of concentric circles on the skin, circles which grew and spread and were carried to other parts of the body by the scratching of the victims. Other men—particularly those who swam, from choice or from necessity, in the shallow waters of bays or streams—developed fungus infections of the ears. Still others were troubled by ringworms essentially similar to those found in the United States, infections which spread over the feet and the hands and crawled up the legs.

These infections could all be cured. But in the tropics the cure was usually a slow process. The constant sweating, induced by Guadalcanal's heat and aggravated by the work the men had to perform, seemed to inhibit cure and to delay healing. Here again the establishment of security on the island brought about a marked reduction in the number of cases of infection. Once men could take precautions, once they could avoid contact with fungus infested earth or water, once they could boil their clothes and bathe frequently, their troubles from such infections began to disappear.

I have already told of the fight against malaria. There was another mosquito-borne disease, dengue, against which there is very little the doctors were able to do.

Dengue or breakbone fever is far less severe than malaria. It is very rarely fatal; I do not believe we have experienced a single death because of dengue throughout the South Pacific. But to its victim it is fully as annoying and as debilitating as malaria. Unlike malaria, dengue is a self-limiting, non-relapsing disease. It is believed that one attack grants the victim several months' immunity.

I speak of dengue from personal experience, for I caught it—a mild attack—during my last stay in Guadalcanal. The disease is spread by a mosquito with the attractive name of *Aedes aegypti*. The mosquito itself is quite an attractive fellow, much better looking than his relative, *Anopheles*, the vector of malaria. But the disease *Aedes* spreads is one of the least attractive illnesses that man is heir to.

It starts with a rise in temperature. At one moment you are going your way, oblivious to the fact that a week or more before you were bitten by *Aedes*. Then suddenly you feel flushed. Despite the sweltering heat the air seems chilly. But you brush it off and think nothing of it until an hour or two later when the initial rash begins to appear. If you have a mild case ("mild," that is, only to the doctors and the corpsmen—the victim never thinks it is mild) the rash may be too slight to be noted. You may miss too the sensations of itching on the palms and the soles of your feet. But then along comes the headache and the pains in your joints and muscles. Your eyes feel tired. Then they feel painful. Soon you wish nothing so much as to close them, for every movement of the eyeballs causes a sharp twinge. At about that point you usually turn in for sick call.

In my case I didn't want to do that. I was living at a hospital anyway and if I got any sicker I could always call a doctor. So I just took to my cot and spent the next four or five days alone with my symptoms. I had watched others have dengue. I had heard them describe the disease many times before. Now I began to realize how thoroughly inadequate is any individual's description of his own pains.

They had told me that for three or four days one runs a temperature. But they did not tell me that during those three days you are quite convinced that you are going to die. They had told me that then the temperature drops for a day or two. But they had not told me that when it does drop you feel light and giddy and find great pleasure in being able to move your limbs again without an instant, startling, stabbing burst of pain. They had told me that the fever comes back after the few hours' interval. But they had not made it clear that in that second bout with the thermometer—while you know you will not die—you find yourself desperately wishing that you would. Finally they had told me that the second spell of fever is short and that once it is over you are well and ready to get back on your feet. But here again, no one had bothered to inform me that, while you may be ready to get on your feet, you can't always be certain of being able to do so. No one had told me that I was likely to lose fifteen pounds in the process nor that my clothes would undoubtedly fail to fit.

So all through those days I stayed on my cot and ate APC capsules—those marvelous combinations of aspirin, phenacitin, and caffein—and tried to keep from letting the doctors know I had the disease because I wanted to be up on my feet again at the first possible moment and didn't want to be fussed over. Then, when it was almost all over, I found that the doctors had known about it most of the time and had been watching me and laughing a little behind my back.

On the last day, when I was well enough to think of getting better, one of them brought me a book on tropical diseases with the pages dog-eared to mark the treatise on dengue. The last paragraph of the article was underlined. It read, "During convalescence a sound wine should be ordered. Nothing is better than a good burgundy."

Burgundy was rather scarce on Guadalcanal but that night the doctor brought me a bottle of Scotch and that was the end of my dengue.

There have been other diseases that trouble the men in the tropics. But while all of them are annoying, and some of them are dangerous, they constitute but a small fraction of those which attack the natives or even the Japanese. For the Navy's preventive medicine has been extremely effective. The men have been educated to effectively avoid most of the avoidable infections. Their good, if plain, diet and their splendid sanitary facilities have made it possible for them to withstand or quickly beat down the diseases they do get.

Even the rumors which fly like mad through any military camp serve to emphasize our relative freedom from the native infections. On almost every island, I heard about men getting yaws, that horrible spirochete disease which causes great sores to arise all over the body. But on every island it was always at some other place that the infection existed. In all the hospitals from the Russells to Auckland I was not able to find a single case of the disease, although I saw it often among natives in the Solomons.

So, too, with filariasis. Before I entered the Solomons I heard stories of men being evacuated with this disease—men who were described as being in such an advanced stage of elephantiasis that they "had to turn them sideways to get them through the plane doors." Investigation disclosed, however, that only twenty-six men, all told, were evacuated from Guadalcanal under the diagnosis "filariasis." These were marines who had been stationed in Samoa before coming to the Solomons. And they were evacuated as a precautionary measure because it was suspected that they *might* have caught the infection. As for their being in an elephantoid state, that rumor was ridiculous on its face. Even the natives who get the disease must have the infection over many years before any swelling manifests itself. Filariasis is another one of the long list that can probably be checked off as making a good, spine-tingling rumor but not much else.

Even leprosy had its rumors. One story made the rounds about two young Army privates who got too friendly with an Indo-Chinese girl in New Caledonia. According to the story, they found out the next day that the girl was an inmate of a leper colony. And the two privates—who had enlisted for the duration and six months—found themselves shipped back to the States for a seven-year incarceration in a Public Health Service leper home.

It was a good creepy story. But it just wasn't true. There are lepers in New Caledonia. But the leprous girl and the two privates were both figments of the imagination. And the men who passed the story on didn't know that one exposure to leprosy would hardly necessitate a seven-year stay in quarantine merely to determine whether or not the young men had been infected.

One of the diseases we didn't get on Guadalcanal was beri-beri. But many of the Japanese suffered acutely from it. The doctors at the Jap prison camps (where, incidentally, the prisoners receive surpassingly fine medical attention) told me that beri-beri was one of the most common diseases among the prisoners, next only to malaria. The principal item of diet of the Japanese was rice and it seems that their quartermaster department supplied them, on Guadalcanal, with polished rice rather than with the hull-intact variety they usually eat at home. Their exact reason for following this procedure is hard to understand. Perhaps it was because the polished product stands up better in shipment and in the heat of the tropics.

At any rate, after three months of living on polished rice and little else and with no supplementary vitamin B_1 dosage, many were the Japs who turned up with the fumbling fingers, the numb feet, and shaky legs of beri-beri. Even after weeks of proper diet in the prison camps, some of these men still showed symptoms of the wasting disease. One prisoner before me fumbled for ten minutes before he succeeded in button-

ing his coat. Others walked with a curious floppy gait. All,
I was told, complained of a numbness which had gradually
spread from their feet through their legs and to the muscles
of the forearm and wrist.

It was on Guadalcanal that I had my few chances to get
an idea of the quality of Japanese medicine. It did not make
an impressive picture. The Japs suffered severely from malaria, dengue, and beri-beri, to mention but three of the many
diseases which troubled them. Dysentery ran wild through
their camps, particularly during the last two months of their
unhappy stay on the island. The doctors apparently did little
or nothing for the common soldier, either because they were
too busy treating the wounded or because the common soldier
is not highly regarded by the caste-ridden Japanese army.
Japanese prisoners never ceased to marvel at the medical
treatment which the American authorities made available to
them. They seldom broke out with admiration at anything
else American. But in this one respect they could not contain
themselves.

Captured Japanese medical stores were likewise unimpressive. Their instruments seemed good—well designed and
well manufactured. But their medicines were strangely crude.
I remember one stack of bottles that was shown to me. Each
bore a label with a great illustration of a healthy, hairy man
—a slant-eyed Charles Atlas. In the picture the man was
flexing his gigantic muscles with his elbows raised high and
his fists near his ears. Below the illustration, in both Japanese
and English, ran the legend:

UNIVERSAL HEALTH ELIXIR
For the Cure of
Weakness, Dizziness, Diarrhea, Malaria, Rheumatism and
Unnatural Desires

It was a sorry testimonial to the integrity of the Japanese doctor and to the intelligence of the Japanese soldier. Even in their palmiest days, our patent medicine men have seldom gone quite so far into the realm of nonsense in designing their own labels.

All through the islands and on the ships I was constantly struck by the amazing bond of sympathy which seemed to exist between the corpsmen and their patients. The men, throughout the Navy and the Marine Corps, refer to the pharmacist's mates as "Doc." This is not merely a form of address. It's a statement of respect.

On Guadalcanal it was easy to see just why this attitude existed, for here you saw men whose lives had been saved—who were at the moment being saved—by the ministrations of the corpsmen. The enlisted men had a friendly, confident respect for the doctors. But it was not always easy for them to forget that doctors are officers and that, even on Guadalcanal, officers are somewhat set apart. Between the enlisted men and the corpsmen however no barriers of rank intervened. The marine private and the ordinary seaman respected the corpsmen—and in some cases revered them—without the pressures or compulsions of rank. Seeing the corpsmen at work or hearing the stories of how they had worked in the front lines and on the ships, one thought one understood both the cause and the measure of the respect which the men meted out to them. But it was only when I went, on my last day before leaving, to the cemetery at Guadalcanal that I came to appreciate fully the devotion of the enlisted man who has seen action, for his own pharmacist's mate, his own "Doc."

The cemetery was a quiet field, a space where the coconut trees had been torn down and where the sun shone brightly on the row upon row of American graves. The earth between the graves was bare and grassless. But the graves themselves blossomed with ferns and floral offerings and almost every stone bore tribute to the memory of an individual, a tribute lovingly inscribed upon it by the men of his company, or ship, or squadron.

The Graves Commission had placed a cross at the head of each mound, a cross identifying the man by name and rank or rate and service. But the uniformity and sadness of these crosses were softened by the other markings, the ones the men erected for their buddies. Many of these involved the labor of whole companies of troops. Some were elaborately cast concrete stones to which were affixed polished aluminum disks, cut from mess plates and carefully inscribed with records of gallantry and tributes from those who still lived. Often the inscriptions were in crude verse in which sincerity of feeling more than made up for weaknesses in metre or rhyme. Men of the flying squadrons had their graves marked by the blade of a propeller, its hub imbedded in concrete. Artillerymen had, as their monuments, gleaming crosses formed of welded brass shell casings. Tarnish seemed never to stain these crosses. You realized why when you saw a marine carefully polishing one such brass marker. He did it once a week.

Down the long rows ran the names of America's melting pot—Wilt, Pushefko, Fabry, Bobo, Lewis, Hinslee, D'Alessio, Anderson, Lecker, Devlin. And scattered among the gunners and pilots, the mechanics and marines, the coast guardsmen and the sailors were graves which bore a special marking.

There was William B. Giebler after whose name one read, "Pharmacist's Mate 2-Cl—USN."

There was Pfc. Henry E. Hamilton after whose name one read, U.S.A. Med. Det. 27.

There was E. L. Hopkins whose grave was marked by a

concrete stone from which arose a cross of .37 millimeter shells. After his name appeared the legend,

Pharmacist's Mate 3-Cl
Killed in Action
1—24—1943

This Stone Erected By His
Fellow Corpsmen.

And there was Pharmacist's Mate 2-Cl E. W. Burns of the Headquarters Company of the 6th Marines. His stone read,

Our Buddy
Killed January 21, 1943
In the Line of Duty.

There were more graves of corpsmen and medics—many more—far more than their proportion among the troops would have led one to expect. But numbers alone did not tell the story. One read it rather in the crude, the *homely* words of the inscriptions, the sincere words like, "Our Buddy." It is significant, I think, that it was upon a corpsman's grave that I found those simplest and truest of all the words of tribute that have ever been written—all the more effective because the inscription was still but half completed. It read—"Greater love hath no man . . ."

The boy who stood beside me, his head bare under the tropic sun, moved his lips to finish the familiar phrase: "Greater love hath no man than that he give up his life for a friend."

CHAPTER X

TULAGI'S HAPPY EXILES

TULAGI, in the Solomons, is undoubtedly one of the least attractive little holes on earth; a few square miles of marsh and swamp and rock and jungle, bathed in perspiration. In your very first hour there you come to understand why our troops have renamed it "Devil's Island." For Tulagi has none of the beauty of the tropics but every last one of the drawbacks, including a few exclusively its own.

Yet it was on sultry, scrubby, out-of-the-way Tulagi that I found one of the finest little naval hospitals in the entire South Pacific, run by six exiled doctors and built by them out of hope and palm leaves and a talent for appropriation. They came to the island one by one, much to the relief—I suspect—of the commanding officers of the hospitals at which they had first been stationed. For Drs. Drees and Smith and Gibbons and Kingston and Ripley and the "Terrible" Terzian were young mavericks, hardly the sort to fit well into the decorum and tight organization of our larger base hospitals to the south. But at Tulagi they found their niche in the sort of place where no one cared what you wore and where no one bossed you around because no one had any more rank than you did.

They came, they saw and they conquered. What they saw was the sad fact that there was no hospital, despite their orders which spoke of operating "the Naval Dispensary at Tulagi." The hospital the marines had maintained there since our invasion had just been pulled out and with it went almost everything in the way of medical facilities the island then possessed. Even the South Sea atmosphere turned out to be on the other islands. All Drees found was the wreckage of battle, strewn over beach and jungle, and a flock of heavy-weight mosquitoes that not only bit you but tried to carry you off. In a previous chapter, I have written of Terzian's and Kingston's malarial control project.

But, as I have said, they conquered. Starting from literally nothing and asking nothing from the outside world, they beat down malaria and dengue and dysentery one by one. They converted their little island outpost from a pesthole into one of the healthiest spots in the entire South Pacific. They built and "borrowed" huts and instruments and plumbing and blankets and heaven knows what else, until they were operating not merely a naval dispensary but a full-fledged hospital, complete with wards and a laboratory and even a fully equipped surgery . . . a surgery in which at least a score of lives were saved that would have otherwise been lost.

They were heroes, if it's heroism to work under bombings, to save lives, to convert things that were never meant for conversion into the heart and body of a first-class hospital. But they didn't act like the solemn, serious heroes of our schoolbooks. Their zest and sense of fun made you forget—half the time—that they were all doctors, good doctors. Yet every time they ran you ragged with their high jinks, all you had to do was to look at their hospital to realize that these happy exiles, for all their defiance of Navy tradition, were the best thing that ever hit Tulagi.

In the beginning, Drees managed to acquire two tents. When Dr. Ripley turned up with a Bard-Parker knife, they figured they had enough in the way of surgical instruments to make a start. So they tacked up a sign, reading "Open for Business," and proceeded to accept any patients who weren't scared away by the scabrous look of the place.

But two measly tents were by no means all I found when I reached the island. For all six of them possessed what "Daddy" Drees quaintly termed a *"strange knack for acquisition."* Their first chance to exercise this knack came about three weeks after they landed, when they found three tin-roofed huts lying crated on the dock, consigned to some outfit on Florida Island. But something had gone wrong and the boxes had been lying at Tulagi for ten days or maybe two weeks. Drees and the others figured that no one could object if they just "borrowed" these huts for a while. So, one moonless night, the six exiles and their corpsmen raided the dock stealthily and moved the crates to their new hospital site. By the time the people who owned the huts woke up to their loss, Tulagi's Naval Dispensary was erected and fairly well filled with patients. For a while it looked like civil war, but you couldn't, after all, throw sick men out of bed. In the end the colonel from Florida Island settled for a bottle of aspirin and "sleeping privileges" at the hospital on his future visits to Tulagi.

It was about this time that they formed the Tulagi County Medical Society. They were all just lieutenants and nobody out-ranked anyone else. But they figured that Dr. Drees had at least a week's seniority on the Island over the rest of them. So they elected him "Daddy" in recognition of that week's lead. Technically, he was the senior medical officer, but they figured that on Tulagi, "Daddy" would be enough of a title.

The Medical Society began to meet each night to discuss "cases" and to plan new acquisitions. There was the time, for instance, that Lou Ripley took up the problem of the Bard-Parker knife. Here they were, he pointed out, with a perfectly good surgical instrument. And still they were sending surgical cases twenty-three miles across the water to Guadalcanal. It just didn't make sense at all, when all they had to do was to build a surgery. Of course they lacked a sterilizer and an operating table and operating lights and perhaps a hundred other surgical instruments. But on the other hand there was that beautiful Bard-Parker knife lying unused in its case, its shining blade sneering a constant challenge and reproach to the exiles.

The Medical Society proceeded to vote Ripley and Gibbons an "appropriation." Early next morning the two surgeons roped off a corner of one of their huts for an operating room. The problem of a sterilizer was solved when Dr. Kingston waltzed in with a pressure cooker which he had "borrowed" from a mess hall at the other end of the island. The operating lights came in the form of six head lights wrenched off some wrecked Robeling amphibians that were lying on the beach. But for a while they were stymied in their search for an operating table.

It was Ripley who solved that problem. After much hammering, he appeared with a perfectly presentable wooden imitation of an operating table. It had four legs, which was all you could ask of any respectable table. And its top was divided into three parts, so hinged that you could prop your patient into any desired position. For a while they were worried about how to keep that top sanitary, but then one of them found another use for the ever-present gasoline tins, and a few hours work unbending these provided enough metal to cover the table with a shiny—and utterly sanitary— tin-plated surface.

The operating room was completed just in time because the Japs came through then with one of their big raids on Tulagi and the little dispensary was flooded with surgical cases which would never have survived a trip "across the slot" to Guadalcanal. But Ripley and Gibbons operated on all of them and every last one pulled through.

Later, when Captain Dearing, the senior medical officer for the area, visited Tulagi he helped them to acquire a set of real operating lights from a ship that had been banged up and was going back to the States. The new lights were far better, of course, than the old auto-headlights, because with the old set the temperature in the surgery often went up to 150° and more. But in at least one instance the heat of the old headlights can probably be credited with saving a life.

That was the case of Paul Brandon Sharpe. Ripley remembered the name because someone had told it to him just before the operation and it kept running through his head like a song for all the two hours he worked on the boy. It was what they call a "belly-case." Paul Sharpe had been a little late crawling into his foxhole and a daisy-cutter had hit him. A daisy-cutter is an anti-personnel bomb that mows a circle along the ground for fifty yards. If you are in your foxhole, the explosion will pass right over you. But the hot stuff caught Paul Brandon Sharpe squarely and churned the poor boy's stomach into bits.

When they brought him in the only thing to do was to sew him up—and to sew fast. There were so many holes that he didn't look just cut up. "He looked," as Ripley put it, "like he had unraveled." The kid was conscious all through the operation because all they could give him was a spinal anaesthetic. They didn't have gas and ether isn't much good in that kind of heat. It just evaporates too fast. But Paul Brandon Sharpe kept joking and teasing the perspiring doctors all the time—nearly two hours—while Ripley and Gibbons worked on him.

After the first fifteen minutes both doctors were sweating in a steady stream. For a while the corpsmen tried to mop their faces, but then they got too busy tending the other patients, of whom there were plenty that day. The doctors couldn't stop their sewing, so there was nothing to do but to let the perspiration drop right into Paul Brandon Sharpe's open abdomen.

They didn't think he stood much of a chance, but after a long time they got the boy all sewed up. That night, when their patient should have gotten some rest, they had to carry him out of the hut and into the dug-out six separate times when the shooting started up again. Yet after all that, when any older man would have just passad away, the kid lived and got better. In the end, he actually walked out of the hospital and down to the dock when the ship came to evacuate him down South. The doctors couldn't quite understand how Paul had survived, for if any man was ever tagged for death, this boy was—even if he had had all the advantages of a real surgery and anaesthesia and antiseptics and everything else they couldn't give him. Most of all, they couldn't figure out why he didn't develop any infection under those conditions.

"We talked about it a lot afterwards," Ripley told me. "Finally, we figured that maybe it was the sweat we poured into him—a sort of saline irrigation. I know it sounds crazy and unscientific, but we are all more than half convinced that it was the heat from those God-awful head-lights that saved Paul Brandon Sharpe's life."

And yet the doctors were not content to call the heat their ally. Somewhere—no one would admit quite where—they acquired the innards of an old refrigerator. And when I left Tulagi they were busily at work rigging up an air-conditioning system that would make their operating room truly a show place of the South Pacific. It was to have been the only air-conditioning plant in the world that also made ice-cream.

The barrel-shaped, tin-roofed huts, though infinitely better than their original tents, were also proving a little too hot to be practicable. The sun beat down on their corrugated roofs until the mere matter of making the patients stay in bed became a constant problem. But here again the doctors turned engineer. They ripped the tin sheeting off the lower

portion of the walls of each hut. They tore up mosquito nettings and tacked them on to the frames for screens. They
arranged slanting boards for louvers so that the rain wouldn't
come in. And huts that had been a torrid 130° in the shade
went down to ninety-five and ninety degrees, temperatures
which are considered cool on Tulagi.

Then they found they needed another ward. There were
no more huts lying around for Daddy Drees to "borrow,"
but nothing in Navy Regulations said that the Tulagi County
Medical Society was forbidden to invent a makeshift solution.
So the doctors hired two hundred native "boys" who swarmed
like ants all over the place for three days. When they retired
from their ant-hill, there stood a great bamboo and coconut-
leaf hut towering over the surrounding wards. It costs hundreds upon hundreds of dollars to build a prefabricated hut
and to transport it from the States. But the labor for the
new ward set the doctors back exactly forty-one dollars. They
never even billed Uncle Sam.

After it was all over, the natives held a celebration and
danced in the hut for another two days. Then they lined up
and Kingston and Terzian took up their hypodermics and
shot each native full of arsenicals for his yaws. The Tulagi
"boys" thought the doctors were the greatest people on earth
after that. And when I first felt the coolness of the Nipa
shelter I began to direct a little of the same feeling towards
the natives. The new ward was at least fifteen degrees cooler
than even the remodeled old ones.

All the patients wanted to move into it and, for a while,
Daddy Drees had the devil of a time keeping his other wards
occupied. In the end he had to institute a seniority system
and every patient had to spend at least four days in the
Quanset huts before he was "promoted" to the coconut palace.

Meanwhile, Gibbons and Ripley had been gradually ac-
quiring a fairly respectable set of surgical instruments. Every

time they would send a corpsman over to Guadalcanal to get some drugs or dressings, he would come back with a knife or scalpel or something else he would "borrow." It wasn't that the boys were dishonest. Their minds played no part in the procedure. It was simply that their hands couldn't stand the idea of a scalpel lying useless in its original package when old Doc Ripley could do such wonderful things with it back in Tulagi.

But there were some bulky instruments, such as retractors, which proved much too big to slip up a sleeve. The matter of retractors played on Daddy Drees' mind so much that the others—in self-protection—conspired never to mention them in his presence. Then came another aerial dog-fight, when the Zeros pounced over the hills and bore down on Tulagi like a swarm of slant-eyed mosquitoes. The doctors had just finished moving all their patients into the foxholes when the trigger-happy kids who ran the island's ack-ack got the bead on a Zero. Six pairs of anxious eyes watched the plane as it shuddered and started to smoke, way up in the sky, then began to spiral slowly down like a leaf falling on a still day.

Six voices, in unison, cried, "Here come our retractors."

The wounded Zero was tantalizingly slow in coming to earth. It drifted off east and for a while it seemed certain that it would fall into the sea, because Tulagi is a mighty small island. The thought of losing those retractors almost broke Daddy Drees' heart, but at last the plane turned back and when it finally came down it skimmed right over the top of the new bamboo hut and landed in a heap, smack in the middle of Halsey Field. The raid wasn't half over then, and shrapnel was still falling all around the place but all the doctors and all the corpsmen and even some of the patients ran out to that wreck. It might have blown up at any second, but no one seemed to think about that until it was all over. In less than five minutes they were all back in the foxholes, but by then they had enough Jap aluminum to make fifty sets of retractors. "And that," said Ripley, "is how we got the best damn set of medical instruments north of New Zealand."

The greatest triumph of Tulagi's medical marauders, however, is recorded in the Annals of the County Medical Society as "The Case of the High Pressure Water System." In the beginning they got along fairly well with a couple of gasoline drums mounted on a platform. But after half a dozen air-raids, the drums were all shot full of holes. They had been plugged up so many times with wooden pegs that they looked like two giant porcupines sitting up there on the platform.

Carl Smith was chosen this time to "do something" and to support his authority they gave him the resplendent title of South Tulagi Water and Sanitation Commissioner. Every night, Smith and his corpsmen would work on the new system. First they took a few of those big fifty gallon gasoline drums down to the SeaBees' shops and got the machinists there to cut them in half with a welding torch. Then, when they took out the metal bung-stoppers, they had something that was a pretty good approximation of a sink. Next, they "acquired" a couple of belly-tanks which some planes had dropped in the jungle during one of the raids. These they rigged up about ten feet off the ground to provide a gravity flow of water.

Everybody thought that was fine except Carl Smith. For Carl was the laziest fellow I have ever known, and he just couldn't see having to fill those tanks every morning. Just beyond the hospital, on a little knoll, another outfit had its camp. These birds had inherited an artesian well and an old British pump. All *their* men had to do every morning was to work that pump for fifteen or twenty minutes and in that way they filled up a five-hundred gallon tank and had running water all day.

Dr. Smith used to look at that tank so long and so jealously that Drees had to warn him not to steal it under any circumstances. But theft was farthest from Smith's thoughts. One dark night Carl and his corpsmen managed to secure a lot of pipe. When all good people were asleep, Smith and his boys sneaked up to the other outfit's tank and tapped a length of pipe into it. They ran their tube, through a trench, back down the hill to the belly-tanks and when morning came there was nothing to show that dirty work had been afoot. The boys on the hill came out and started to work their pump as per usual. But somehow that morning the pump seemed slow. It was weeks before they found out that gravity was in a conspiracy to make them do an extra twenty minutes of pumping every day.

I had come to Tulagi as a serious-minded medical correspondent, fresh from my visits to the beautifully built and smoothly run base hospitals that the Navy has erected all through the islands to the rear of the Solomons combat zone. I left Tulagi still dazed and goggle-eyed after my stay with the happy exiles. For every hour I had spent with them left me more astonished at their ingenuity. With vigor and with humor, these youngsters had managed to scrape odds and ends together, had contrived to build a smoothly running hospital where not even the ghost of a dispensary had stood before. Moreover, they had actually had fun doing it. It wasn't the way the book said things ought to be done but, rules or no rules, it worked.

Just before I left the South Pacific, I learned that the little band had been split up. The makeshift hospital that was the Naval Dispensary there has by now probably been replaced by a modern installation complete with all the trimmings from air-conditioning to gold braid. Which is—perhaps—as it should be. X-rays and autoclaves and all the other burnished paraphernalia of a modern hospital can make life a lot easier for the Navy's doctors and survival a lot more certain for the men they treat.

But somehow, I can't help regretting the passing of the Tulagi County Medical Society—the craziest, most disrespectful, ingenious, happy-go-lucky and—withal—most effective batch of young doctors I ever hope to see. I find myself hoping that they haven't been sent to the kind of place where you have to wear Navy blues and say "Yes, sir" to the Admiral. For their sake and for the Navy's, I like to think that they have found a new Tulagi—somewhere up the line— and gotten themselves re-exiled to another jungle hole where nothing is done according to Navy Regulations, but everything gets done pretty well nonetheless.

CHAPTER XI

"BASE DASH"

AFTER the Russells and Guadalcanal it was all down-hill. I was on my way out now and it didn't matter how long it took to get out; the sun shone brighter and people seemed nicer. The tropics do that to you. While you're headed away from home you don't fully realize how bad the tropics are. You stand the rain and the heat and the sameness of the food, you stand the mud and the dirt and the knowledge that death might catch up with you any time. If you are a combatant you stand an added fear which I knew only during air raids, the ever-pressing knowledge that you are going to have to meet the Jap and that it won't be pleasant for either of you.

But once you have done your job and you head away from the war zone, once you have got a down-hill run, only then do you realize the strain you have been bearing. The pressure lifts off your compressed nerves and you feel every single separate cell of you expand and breathe again.

I had heard men talk of this before. I had thought I understood them. But it wasn't until I got over my dengue and put all of me—except for the lost pounds—onto a SCAT plane and headed for the lower Hebrides; it wasn't until then that I really knew what these men had been talking about.

Even now, I doubt whether words alone can convey more than a little bit of the feeling. Just take whatever impression you get of it and imagine it multiplied by twenty or thirty times. Then you will begin to get as much of an idea of what it is like as anyone can who hasn't been there.

I had left Guadalcanal before. But those times I knew I would be going back. This time it was different. I was light as a feather. I helped push the plane off the ground. I floated around up in space in perfect communion with all the other evacuees. I knew now, in my bones as well as in my mind, why the sick and wounded boys were all smiling. They smiled all the time—at anything and at nothing at all. And they weren't being heroic, they weren't being storybook heroes. They were just damn glad to be going away from the tropics and away from the war, even if only for a little while.

It was in this manic state that I arrived at Base Dash.* I introduced myself to the hospital's admissions officer and, once he had loaded the patients on the ambulances, we went lurching after them in his jeep. The road ran for miles through coffee, coconut, and copra plantations. Then it dipped down into the little European town and came out on the other side to climb for more miles, through stretches of alternating jungle and plantation. It was a good road— the best I had seen in the tropic islands—but there was no fun in navigating it at fifty miles an hour in a jeep that had been sired by a kangaroo. When we finally drew up at the hospital, I felt ready for a bed in one of the wards.

Instead, I was welcomed as I never had been before, anywhere else in the hospitable South Pacific. Captain John E.

* Its name of course wasn't Base Dash. The place had a name and a number. I am sure the Japs knew much more about it than just its number because their spy system throughout all the South Pacific islands is pretty effective. It ought to be; they built it up for years. But so far as I know this particular hospital has never been localized and identified in the public press. So just to keep my nose clean with Navy Public Relations I will have to call it "Base Dash."

Porter, the commanding officer, sat me down and gave me a cigarette. His executive officer, Commander Oliver W. Butler, offered me a cigar. Commander W. H. Leake lit it for me. Then all three gentlemen, in a single breath, said, "What can we do for you?"

They meant it too. It wasn't merely that my credentials and letters of introduction said that they should extend to me every courtesy. It was much more than that. The welcome I had received applied with equal vigor and emphasis to every visitor and every patient. Base Dash was simply the most hospitable place in the entire South Pacific.

Inside of half an hour I had been assigned a bed in one of the airy, doctors' huts which stood at the edge of the slope, overlooking miles of jungle and winding bays. My soiled clothes were on the way to the laundry—including even the shirt and socks which I wore on arrival. Commander Gene Owen, who occupied the bed to my right, lent me one of his shirts. Lieutenant Commander James MacNish, who had the left-hand bed, rummaged into his sea-chest and brought out socks and handkerchiefs. Then both of them waltzed me off to the officers' club for the first real drink—with real ice— I had had in months. After the second drink, I tried to buy a round but I was promptly put in my place. "Your money is no good here," they told me. And they, too, meant it.

The hospital had looked trim and businesslike as I drove through the gates and past the long rows of low, gray-painted buildings. It became all the more impressive when I learned how this neatly finished place had become that way.

The doctors had left the states in April, 1942—thirty-three of them—with 239 hospital corpsmen. On May 4, 1942, they reached their destination and began their mission: to establish the first advanced base hospital in the entire South Pacific. At that time the Japs were already at Tulagi. And between Base Dash and the Japs there was nothing but water and islands—and none too much of that. When they unloaded their gear there was no way in which these men could be certain that they were not bringing a hospital for the Japanese rather than for Americans.

In theory, unloading operations are supposed to be carried on by engineering troops specially trained for such purposes. In practice—they learned immediately—you do your own unloading and your own building when you establish a base. Medical officers were assigned to duties as deck officers, supervising the removal of cargo from the holds, the lighterage, and the unloading and trucking operations ashore. The hospital corpsmen acted as stevedores, winchmen, truck drivers, and boat crews. They worked round the clock, these amateurs, bringing forty thousand tons of cargo out of the holds and up into the hills in record time. And they did it all without a single injury.

Meanwhile, from the second day onward, they had the hospital in operation and accepting patients. In the small Franco-British town—it would hardly have passed as a village in the States—they took over the tiny civilian hospital, the courthouse, a church, and eight residences. And they hospitalized 450 patients whom they received from the scattered tent dispensaries of the units already on the island and from the sick bays of the ships in the harbor.

The doctors all worked part-time in this temporary hospital. The rest of their time was spent on the sixty-acre tract, five hundred feet up in the hills, which had been selected for the permanent hospital's site. It was one of the most beautiful locations that could have been chosen, high and relatively dry, with long rows of coconut palms for shade and a splendid view of great expanses of the incredible blue and jade and orange waters of the Coral Sea. It was also one of the most healthful of sites: malaria free, cool at night—

at least by contrast with the heat of the days—and breeze-swept sometimes, during what the doctors wistfully called the "winter" season.

On this tract, the doctors and their corpsmen—with some aid, but none too much, from a SeaBee construction battalion—erected 203 building units. There were thirty great wards; twelve for medical cases, fourteen for surgical cases and four isolation wards. Two complete groups of little houses, widely separated from each other, formed the surgical units. Each consisted of two operating rooms, a sterilizer room and a wash room, and each was surrounded by a revetment of sand-bags and sod.

Covered boardwalks were built, connecting all the wards and leading on to the laundries, the commissaries, the club-rooms, the doctors', nurses', and corpsmen's quarters and the x-ray, dental, and laboratory buildings.

A curved slope was converted into an outdoor movie am-phitheater. Here at night the patients used to gather, making a weird picture as they sat in their hospital bathrobes, in long, even rows punctuated here or there by a crutch or an upraised cast. I had seen all their movies (after a while with the Navy you have seen all the movies there are) but the droning familiar talk and singing of the sound tracks made a pleasant counterpoint to the beating of my typewriter.

For at Base Dash I had work to do, plenty of work for a change. I had found a gold mine of information; detailed, carefully compiled records and analyses. The hospital had just completed its first year of duty in the field and all the doctors were engaged in preparing a great symposium, an-alyzing every phase of their work. Captain Porter and Com-mander Leake made these papers available to me and I spent my evenings abstracting their data into my notes. Daytimes, when I toured the wards and interviewed the men who had done the work and written the papers, I was far better able to understand their problems and to discuss them because of the detailed view I had obtained from their records and reports.

The hospital had treated—and was still treating—a very substantial portion of all the casualties from the Solomons. Until Joel White's unit had been established somewhat further up the line, it had been the first point of evacuation for the entire area. Even after Joel White was ready to receive casualties, Base Dash still took fully half the load.

Several of the men who had come down from Guadalcanal with me were such patients, boys with fractures, chest wounds or bullet wounds of the soft tissues. When they arrived at the hospital they were sent immediately to a receiving and examining room, where their dressings were opened and their injuries classified and recorded. Then they passed on, via the x-ray rooms, to the various specialized wards.

In the orthopedic ward, to which all fractures of the extremities were taken, I watched one G. I. Joe arrive. First the doctor came in and made a thorough examination of the fractured leg. This he did even while the corpsmen and a nurse were removing the boy's dirt-caked uniform and preparing him for a bath. The patient was a young soldier, in good condition, and he seemed to enjoy the unexpected attentions he was receiving. He had hardly been dressed and tucked into bed before another corpsman turned up with a tray of hot soup and chocolate. Everybody stood round him while he ate, including several of the ambulatory patients who hobbled up on casts to greet the new arrival. Then he was given ten grains of sulfathiazole. Morphine was omitted since he was not in pain.

That afternoon, the boy was taken to surgery. On the table his splint was gently removed and the traction on his leg was maintained, by hand, by one of the corpsmen who stood at the foot of the operating table. Meanwhile, the skin around his wound was shaved and scrubbed in preparation for the débridement—the necessary excision of injured flesh— and the final setting of his fracture. When the doctors set to work, they first gave him pentothal sodium anaesthesia, feeding it into his vein drop by drop from a hypodermic while the lad counted slowly—one, two, three—. When he reached eighteen the counting stopped and the boy was asleep.

A skeletal pin was inserted at the lower part of the injured leg and the traction devices attached to it, holding the leg tautly in place. Then débridement began, a careful cutting away of the devitalized tissue and an equally careful avoidance of the uninjured flesh. When the doctor had finished and was irrigating the open wound, he had a clean dish-shaped cavity at the bottom of which one could see the fractured bone.

A few free bone fragments were removed and the fracture was carefully set into alignment. Then all the raw surfaces were dusted with crystalline sulfanilamide and the wound was gently filled with strips of vaseline-impregnated gauze. Small dry dressings were applied over this and the leg was finally immobilized with heavy, molded wire splints.

Then the boy was sent back to the ward, placed in bed and his leg set in traction once again. Later, the doctors would apply their cast in bed, still maintaining the skeletal traction until the plaster had firmly set.

In all, at Base Dash, they handled 722 such compound fractures. Nearly a third of the men had two or more fractures which were treated simultaneously in operations such as I had just witnessed. The vast majority of these men had reached the hospital after a five- to seven-hour airplane trip, from half a day to two full days after being injured. And yet of all that vast number—of all those men hit and torn by bullets, by bombs, by shells, or by shrapnel—only nine died. Perhaps half of all the fracture cases walked away from Base Dash—thirty or sixty or ninety days after they came in on their stretchers—walked away, down to the dock and back to duty with the Navy or the Marines.

In their reports the doctors were modest and dispassionate. They did not ascribe the record they had achieved to the quality of their surgery. Instead they looked for reasons, for special peculiarities of the situation or the patients, which might explain their unusual success. For unusual it was, even in this war where surgery on every front has been establishing enviable records. In the last war death rates from fractures ran 40 per cent and higher!

One of the peculiarities they commented upon was the almost uniformly good alignment of the fractured bones when the patients arrived. Men came in with massive wounds beneath the torn flesh in which the doctors found hundreds of shattered fragments of bone. Yet the main portions of the fractured bones were still in line—as they almost never are when men are injured in industrial accidents or automobile or railroad wrecks. This excellent positioning of the fragments—which, to be sure, accounted in some measure for the excellent results the doctors obtained—they attributed first of all to the battle field doctors and corpsmen, the men who first splinted these wounds hundreds of miles up the line. But they noted another phenomenon as well. The terrific impact of high velocity bullets and shrapnel fragments seemed to induce a muscular paralysis—they called it *stupeur musculaire*—a paralysis which often served to save the injured limb. For the paralyzed muscles failed to pull the bones around as they might otherwise have done.

One of the doctors who played a major part in the orthopedic work at Base Dash was Commander Henry Howard

Kessler. Dr. Kessler, who served for many years as the medical director of the New Jersey Rehabilitation Clinic, has specialized in the rehabilitation of the crippled and disabled. To him were brought most of the small group of amputations which had to be performed. There were only thirty-nine of these all told—a figure which in itself is a remarkable testimonial to the quality of the early medical service which was given to the wounded in the field. Most of the amputations were performed on gunshot wounds which had caused irreparable injury to the main blood vessels or extremely extensive loss and destruction of tissue.

Kessler was the ideal man for such work, a patient, kindly, roly-poly creature who somehow inspired great confidence by the very simplicity of his manner. You felt as you watched him work that you would hate to be on his operating table. But if anyone had to take your leg off and you had the choice of doctors, Kessler was the man you'd pick.

The surgeon in a military post is seldom quite as free in his work as he has been in civil life. He must consider not only the individual patient but the fact that scores of others may be awaiting his service. Sometimes—though, fortunately, very rarely—he must pass up a badly injured man, requiring hours of work, because his labors may be needed by ten or twenty other men who can be returned to duty.

But once an amputation was decided upon, the surgeons at Base Dash assumed a twofold responsibility. On the one hand they were concerned with life-saving—the removal of the gangrenous infected or mutilated limb. This was the responsibility they owed to every patient no matter what his injury. But at the same time they felt a special responsibility toward the man who would leave their operating theater minus an arm or a leg. To him their duty was, they knew, to provide much more than life itself. They had to so plan their operations that after the amputation each man would still possess a stump to which a suitable artificial limb —a prosthesis—could be attached.

Men like Kessler had seen the amputations of the last war, not only among the American troops but among Europeans as well. They knew what happened to men whose lives were saved only to leave them helpless cripples, unfit for work and unfit for living. And they were resolved that nothing which they did at Base Dash—and nothing which they might leave undone—would ever contribute toward setting any American upon that horrible road.

Kessler led me up to an understanding of his operations by first describing the whole history of amputations. Generations ago, before artificial limbs had reached their present state of perfection, most amputations contemplated the use of a peg leg. The only function of the prosthesis was to support a man's weight. Because this was so, leg amputations were planned to secure heavy pads of flesh at the end of the stump, pads which could take the constant hammering impact that came with every step upon the wooden leg.

Today, the amputation of a leg calls for far more skill on the part of the physician. But its end result is a stump to which can be attached an artificial leg which will be supported by the side surfaces of the stump and by specially planned pressure-bearing areas. The planning of such an amputation is a complex engineering job. The orthopedic surgeon selects the site of amputation so that the stump will be of exactly the proper length to provide a maximum usefulness for the new leg. He knows that too long a stump may be just as inadequate as too short a one and he therefore adjusts his planning both to the condition of the wounded limb and to the height and weight and other characteristics of the man on whom he is working.

I have seen some of Kessler's legless patients at Base Dash when they received their first provisional prostheses, plaster pylons on which they learned to balance themselves and to walk. And seeing them, I have understood how Kessler could promise—and they could believe—that when they returned to the States and got their shapely leather and aluminum legs—shoes and all—they would be able not only to walk again but to run, to jump, and even to dance.

Amputations of the arms present an even more acute problem. It is relatively simple to reproduce the lost function of a leg by artificial means—for that function is primarily one of weight-bearing. The functions of the hand and arm—grasping, holding, twisting, and turning—are much more difficult to attain with an artificial limb. They cannot be fully duplicated. At best they can only be imitated.

But here, a few men at Base Dash were lucky—if ever a man who loses an arm can be justly described by that term. For Commander Kessler is the master of the difficult cineplastic technique, a form of operation which he introduced and developed in the United States.

Until the development of cineplastic work the man who lost an arm had the dubious choice of two types of prosthetic appliances. He could use a "cosmetic" arm, for appearance only but without any prehensile function. Sometimes these were equipped with a rubber hand which he could place in various positions with the aid of his good hand. As a second choice, there was the mechanical arm, one with a hand mechanism activated by a cord attached to the opposite shoulder. By moving both the artificial and the natural arms the wearer of such a contrivance could produce a pull on this cord which opened the hand mechanism. Relaxing his natural arm released the cord and permitted a spring to close the hand. Sometimes these appliances sacrificed cosmetic advantages in favor of removable hooks which permitted the wearer to perform a wider range of pulling operations.

The limitations of such prostheses are obvious and it was to overcome these limitations that the cineplastic technique was developed. The operation is performed in several stages. First comes the direct amputation. Some weeks later, after the stump has healed, the patient is examined and two muscles in the stump are selected and marked out. Then, under a general anaesthetic, these muscles are cut and pierced and a tube of skin is inserted into each of them.

As the wound heals, the skin tube grows to form a continuous part of the skin of the arm stumps, a part into which wood or ivory pegs may be placed. The patient is able to operate an artificial limb with great agility by using his own muscles as the motor force. With some training he soon attains a high degree of prehensile ability, approaching—though never, of course, fully equaling—the abilities of a normal arm and hand.

This operation Kessler performed on three of his patients at Base Dash. In two of these cases it had been necessary to amputate both arms. The first two of the patients had already left the hospital when I arrived, going on to the United States to receive their artificial limbs and to return to civilian life. One of them, a Marine sergeant, was still remembered at the hospital; remembered both for his guts and for the vigor with which he expressed his opinions. When the amputations were performed on him he was too weak to be fully conscious of what was going on. In the days which followed he went through the normal and expected period of despair. But when he climbed the operating table the second time his comment was, "Gee, you guys sure show me a lot of attention," and when he left the hospital it was with a roll of plans under his arms—he had drawn with a pencil in his mouth—plans for the gas station he expected to operate in his own home town.

The third case I saw, an army man who was just recovering from his second operation. The stump of one arm—cut between the elbow and the shoulder—had been equipped with cineplastic motors. The other arm, amputated a few inches above the wrist, had been treated by another technique in which the two bones of the arm had been formed into pincer-like fingers. These had already healed and he was able to use them to grasp things with, though he would not obtain his proper prosthesic hands until he reached the States.

When I saw him he was seated on a bench outside the ward, reading a reprint of an article by Kessler, which one of the corpsmen had obtained for him. The article was profusely illustrated with pictures of Kessler's industrial-accident patients shown working saws, planes, and drills, writing with pencils and even in one case playing a violin. When I came into sight the young man called me over.

"Say, Doc," he asked—many of the patients called me "Doc," assuming that any visitor was a doctor—"does the fiddle come with the new arm?"

Then he smiled and gave me a broad wink and everyone around him laughed. Until then I had thought of amputations as gruesome and of men without arms as tortured victims of the war. As I walked away I wasn't quite so sure. For Kessler had given this boy more than just an artificial limb. The kid had something to look forward to and he no longer pitied himself. Only men who feel they can face the world can joke that way about their difficulties.

Base Dash had its lighter moments, too, for by no means all of its cases were the maimed nor even the wounded. As in all the other hospitals I visited, one felt that his was not an unhappy place. The men were bored, perhaps. They could think of an infinite number of places in which they would rather be—most of them east of Frisco. But while they were in the hospital, they enjoyed themselves—resting, playing cards, listening to the radio, or telling each other, over and over again, about their experiences.

Late afternoons and evenings fell for me into a pleasing routine. I would be typing away in the pleasant hut that I shared with Gene Owen and Jim MacNish. Then the doctors would come back from their work and we—like the patients—would sit around and shoot the breeze. The doctors would tell me about their cases, or tip me off to where the more interesting patients were to be found. Then their conversation would drift to talk of home and of their days of civilian practice. Often other doctors would come in and eight or ten of us would gather in a medical bull-session in which I was accepted more out of politeness than because I had anything to contribute to the highly technical conversation.

The sun would set and the short tropic twilight would find us all ambling over to the officers' club for a drink before dinner. At those times you hardly realized—in officers' country—that there was a great hospital behind us and a great war all around. After supper we would drift again to the club to sit with the nurses over a glass of beer, to watch the movies or—most often—to return to the hut and shoot the breeze again.

Sometimes the arguments became vigorous, almost heated, as when the men took sides in discussing socialized medicine with most of the younger doctors ardently in favor of it and most of the older men saying that it wouldn't work. But arguments had a different quality out there in the Pacific. You noticed it wherever you went. Somehow, everybody granted to everyone else the right to his opinion no matter how bizarre. They differed with each other carefully, gingerly, without hard feelings, as if having an opinion and sticking up for it and letting the other man have his was one of the things for which they had all gone out to the Pacific.

Many a time, in the wards among the enlisted men, I have seen the same thing happen. It is one of the most cheering phenomena to come out of the war. For the Army and Navy and the Marine Corps may have regimented and molded our young men for the duration. But their minds are freer than ever.

I went with Gene Owen through his burn ward, very much like the burn ward in Auckland, a quiet place where people talked in whispers as if even the rasping of a voice would set exposed nerves a-tingling.

They had had nearly a hundred burn cases at Base Dash, from minor injuries to practically full body burns. Only two had died, men who arrived at the hospital in a moribund state. Two-thirds of the rest were sufficiently severe to require further evacuation—to New Zealand or to the States. But the men who remained in the burn ward—what Owen called the minor cases—would for the most part have been rated as severe burns at any hospital in the States.

One of them was an enlisted aviator, a sergeant who had crashed with his pilot and been thrown free only to crawl back into the burning plane in a vain attempt to rescue the other man. Now, he was recovering, under Owen's gentle treatment, from the burns of flaming 100-octane gasoline which had seared most of his back and arms and shoulders. The wreck had occurred not far from the hospital and the young flyer had been brought to the operating room quickly. The burned skin which hung from him in gray leathery slivers had been slowly picked away and the raw flesh had been sprayed with crystalline sulfathiazole powder. Then the injured areas had been covered with a thin layer of tannic acid jelly and the man had been placed under a heat cradle.

Now, three weeks later, almost all of the skin had grown back, pink and fresh, with only here and there a small, bloody bleb where the final healing was yet to be completed. Only a few years ago a case like this would invariably have been treated with skin grafts, a long and painful process. Today less and less of such grafting seems to be necessary—provided adequate preliminary treatment has been given. Even in the field or at sea, with conditions at their worst, such treatment seems almost always to be given by virtually every Navy doctor.

In MacNish's ward I found the explanation of one condition that had been puzzling me throughout my months in the South Pacific; the almost total absence of venereal disease. Jim MacNish was one of the urologists of the hospital, the doctors whose special field is the treatment of injuries and diseases of the genitals, the urinary tract, and the kidneys.

Of all the thousands of patients treated at Base Dash, there were only four cases of acute gonorrhea and sixteen of chronic gonorrhea, the latter having probably been developed in the States. There was not a single case of primary syphilis and the two cases of secondary syphilis which cropped up were likewise contracted prior to leaving the States.

Venereal diseases, a major problem in any armed force almost anywhere else in the world, were simply not a problem in the tropic islands. For sex was in suspended animation. Except for the natives, the nearest women were thousands of miles away. And the native women seemed to hold very little attraction for the boys from Keokuk and Ashtabula.

Even in New Zealand there seemed to be very little, if any, venereal infection among the armed forces we had sent into that country. The ship that brought me north from Auckland had been in port—with its men having nightly liberty—for fifteen days. Yet not a single case of venereal disease made itself manifest during that time nor in the following week of our trip northward.

MacNish explained the phenomenon in several ways. He pointed out that the long voyage from the States served to expose—and thus to quarantine—almost every case of venereal disease which a man may have contracted before leaving the continental United States. New Zealand itself had had a relatively low incidence of both syphilis and gonorrhea before the war. The index had probably fallen still lower in the first years of the war, when so many of that country's men were fighting in Egypt and the Middle East. Thus, it would seem that our men were neither bringing these diseases into the area to any great degree nor were they widely exposed to venereal infections among the local population. As MacNish put it, "Thank God. We have enough to deal with as it is."

The dentists at Base Dash were like dentists everywhere in the Navy—the handiest people to have around. Three of them had come out from the States with the original hospital group. They brought with them a well-equipped dental department which, however, lacked a prosthetic laboratory. In that first year they had held 7,368 chair sittings. They had made 3,220 fillings, performed 982 extractions, removed ninety-four impacted teeth, made 1,620 x-ray examinations and reduced forty-four jaw fractures.

Yet this was but a tiny fraction of their work. For they had also found the time to build themselves a complete dental laboratory. They had constructed a host of complex laboratory instruments—flasks, duplicators, hinge articulators, and bench presses. They had built a lathe from the motor of a broken-down flour-sifter. They made a vibrator out of an automobile coil, a .75 millimeter shell casing and a piece of aluminum taken from a wrecked plane.

With this improvised equipment they made gold inlays, bridges, crowns, and plates and repaired scores of broken dentures. Then they went outside their own field—once again, after the usual manner of Navy dentists—and made splints for fractured noses, restored eye-glass frames, fixed watch crystals, repaired rings, and performed a thousand-and-one other minor repair jobs. A dentist at Base Dash or elsewhere in the Navy is never troubled by boredom.

The day I left the hospital the staff held one of its weekly medical conferences. For even here, eight thousand miles from home, the doctors kept up the scholarly practice of self-education. Men continued to write papers and to read them, to listen attentively and to comment and criticize politely but incisively.

In part, this may explain the amazing record that Base Dash achieved. For of all the thousands of sick and wounded men who passed through its wards, fewer than three out of every thousand died! The vast majority went on to return to duty: reconditioned, rehabilitated, refed and refreshed.

CHAPTER XII

THE PSYCHIATRISTS' WAR

FOR many years before the war, psychiatrists were gravely and frankly worried about the effect of modern warfare on the mental condition of the soldier. They knew how tremendous a problem mental casualties had presented in the first World War. They knew how many thousands of "shell-shocked" psychiatric casualties still filled our veterans' hospitals fifteen and twenty years after the Armistice. And they knew, too, that in the interval between conflicts, warfare had become more terrible than ever before.

The psychiatrists were aware that their infant branch of medicine had progressed far in the years since 1918. They had reason to hope that in this war the psychiatric casualty would no longer be treated—as he had been in earlier wars— as a malingerer, a "yellow" coward who was shirking his duty. This change in attitude, this willingness, among most officers in the Army and the Navy, to recognize the mental casualty as a sick man requiring doctoring quite as much as any other wounded man—this they knew would tend to counterbalance, to a degree, the increased intensity of warfare. Yet during our first year in the war—and to some extent even today—most of the published comments on war psychiatry have been of the most lugubrious and dismal variety.

I was still under the influence of such thinking when I joined the *Relief*. Much of what I saw on that ship was to fortify my forebodings. Lieutenant Commander Chester

Reynolds, the *Relief's* psychiatrist, anticipated the necessity of handling a large number of psychiatric casualties. Wisely, he was preparing for any contingency. He and his corpsmen were busy, during most of our outward journey, in rebuilding the *Relief's* so-called "locked ward." The very term "locked ward" was a frightening one. It suggested the need for handling men driven violently insane, men with a suicidal mania, who might have to be restrained behind bars to prevent their self-destruction.

The "locked ward" itself did not prove half as frightening as its crude and—I should point out—unofficial name. It was a large, airy compartment on the main deck, a room of widely spaced bunks that would have been almost a pleasant place in which to be sick. But you could not escape a shudder as you entered it, for a heavy metal-lattice door closed behind you. The corpsmen, practicing to develop the habit, always locked the door with a great clanking of keys. The port holes, you noticed, were unostentatiously—but very effectively—barred.

Even more disquieting were the training lectures which Reynolds and the psychiatric nurse, Miss Florence Asheld, delivered to the psychiatric corpsmen. Dr. Reynolds was very careful to point out, at the start of each lecture, that most mental casualties would never reach the locked ward. But such an explanation took only a minute. The rest of each period was given over, quite properly, to a careful indoctrination of the corpsmen in the work they might have to perform in handling violent cases.

Little Miss Asheld—she weighed 114 pounds and stood five foot four—demonstrated to the specially selected, muscular corpsmen, all the tricks of the trade. She showed them how to subdue a violent patient—without hurting the patient but without endangering themselves. She taught them the art of snapping a wet towel around the wrist to quickly im-

mobilize a manic case. She made them practice the compli-
cated technique of placing a patient in a cold pack. Repeatedly
the boys wrapped each other in the long wet sheets, learning
by practice how to ensure immobility for the patient.

All of the lessons were essential and wise. They sought to
prepare the corpsmen for what they might have to do. But
the overall effect of this teaching could only serve to reinforce the impression that the most horrible—and possibly the
most frequent—of all the casualties I would see would be
the mental cases.

It was only after I had visited the hospitals in New Caledonia and after I had seen mental cases on the *Solace* that I
began to realize that the impressions gained on the *Relief*
gave me a woefully misleading picture of the actual situation.
For in Noumea, on the *Solace,* and in Auckland—and later,
at all the stations up to the Russells—the psychiatric patients
I saw were by no means the "crazy" men I had been led to
expect.

True there were a few psychotic types, men who for varying periods had to be kept under some form of restraint.
Even with these, the periods were usually short and the restraints mild. Most of these cases—I found, when I went to
the records—were not battle casualties at all. They were men
whose heredity and environment combined to make them
candidates for a psychiatric ward, even if there had been no
war. Their work in the armed forces had merely precipitated their mental difficulties, just as they might have been
precipitated—sooner probably rather than later—in civil life.

The vast majority of the other mental patients were so-
called psycho-neurotics—sick, tired, emaciated, worn out, jit-
tery men who had proved temporarily unable to stand the
strains of battle or the anticipations of combat. Such men
needed no restraints. They were not violent. On the contrary,

most of them were both physically and mentally incapable of any violence. They needed sleep, rest, good food, a chance to resolve the conflicts in their own minds and—most of all —some friendly understanding, some reassurance that would convince them that they were not cowards, that they had not betrayed their comrades by succumbing to the strain.

As I talked with these men, in their quiet sunny wards or lolling on the lawns in Auckland, I began to realize that these breakdowns were far different from those of civil life. And when I checked the records and spent long hours with the kind and understanding psychiatrists, I came gradually to see how these breakdowns occurred and just how great was the medical victory which the psychiatrists were achieving in curing them.

Many of these cases were men who had fought at Guadalcanal. From their own stories, from their records and from the things the doctors told me, I began to get a new picture of that battle, a point of view essentially different from that of most war correspondents. To the military psychiatrist Guadalcanal was not merely a tale of individual heroics and delicate strategy. It was, rather, a long drawn-out ordeal in which the minds of normal, healthy young Americans were subjected to every imaginable type of strain. Let me try to redescribe that battle, to put into words the way these men saw it.

On the first day of attack, a few thousand marines landed at palm-fringed Lunga Beach. Their landing had been preceded by a heavy naval bombardment which drove the Japs back into the hills. With little opposition they worked their way two or three miles inland, through the straight-aisled coconut groves, to Henderson Field.

The victory seemed almost too easy. It was, in fact, too good to be true. Within a day or two, it became apparent that the first day's successes were but the beginning of a very long and difficult battle.

The Japs, who had retreated into the hills to avoid the worst of the naval bombardment, now began to come back and offer combat. But the fight they offered was not what most of the marines had expected. Many a man later told how Japanese treachery, trickery, and their tactics of infiltration came to him as an unexpected shock. This was true, not only of the enlisted men, but of many of the officers as well.

Despite all the precedents of Bataan and the Malayan campaign, most of the men could not believe all they had heard until they learned about Japanese warfare through their own bitter experience. The psychology of the Jap soldier who would fight in a cave but would not surrender was something that surprised the men; to the point where they completely overlooked their own habit of not surrendering.

Yet, on those first few days, the general feeling on Guadalcanal was one of self-congratulation. The marines had been given a job and they had done it well. The men in the ranks, at least, felt that they now had only to hold the perimeter of Henderson Field for a few days, until—in accordance with all the dictates of tradition—the Army arrived to take over.

Almost immediately, the men found themselves in a situation for which their training had not fully prepared them. Instead of being the attackers, they were the besieged, hemmed in on a few square miles of tropical jungle and exposed coconut plantation. The Jap fleet turned up, and while the Navy fought that fleet to a standstill and better, the marines on the island saw their small store of supplies dwindling. The transports which had brought them had gone, and the new fleet which they expected to bring the relieving Army did not heave into sight.

A feeling of isolation came over many of the men. For

some this merged into a feeling of betrayal, as if they had been sent on a fruitless mission and then abandoned to their fate. For most of the troops, however, the sense of isolation served naturally to improve morale. They were marines. They didn't need any help from anyone. If necessary, they would hold the field till hell froze over.

As the days went by, new and even more adverse factors entered the picture. The marines had been trained for active warfare, trained to *charge* into the face of danger. They began to find it a very different thing to have to *sit* in the face of danger. Yet this they had to do all day around the perimeter of the field. And at night, as well, when the "Tokyo Express" came in close to shore to shell their bivouacs. Night after night, with careful calculation for psychological effect, the Japanese sent "Washing-Machine Charley" groaning overhead to drive the tired men from their tents, to rob them of sleep and to force them into the malarial wetness of the shallow foxholes.

Meanwhile, two more Jap allies entered the picture, hunger and malaria. Malaria did not make its appearance during the first few days. It never does. Thus some of the men grew careless and omitted their daily prophylactic dose of atabrin. An increasing number of them began to come down with the disease, while others were debilitated by dysentery and dengue. Fighting and living in the jungle slime, they fell victim to a host of other minor diseases, none of them lethal but all irritating.

Hunger came when the men began to exhaust the relatively small stock of supplies they had been able to move onto the beach in the first few days. It came all the sooner because part of that stock was destroyed in the shelling and bombings. It was staved off through the use of captured stores of Jap rice and barley. But while Japanese might be able to live on such a diet, it was something for which Americans had no taste. A line in one of the many poems composed on the island aptly sums up the men's feeling towards such fare. It speaks of *"chocolate like lead for our daily bread and worms in the rice for meat."*

Thus, throughout the last weeks of August and all of September and October and November, a group of young, healthy, hardened, and well-trained Americans found themselves hammered from every side by a combination of adverse circumstances such as few armies have ever successfully met before; a situation in which almost every factor combined to induce mental breakdowns. Physically, the men were exhausted by the rigors of a battle which they had endured without relief for ten and twelve weeks at a stretch. The area into which they were penned was so small that even their periods "back of the lines" did not serve to free them from the constant danger of bombing, shelling, and attack by infiltrating Japanese. Added to the wear of battle were the debilitating effects of heat, disease, and hunger. Small wonder, then, that when I surveyed the records of some 350 war neurosis cases who were evacuated from Guadalcanal, I found an average loss of weight in excess of twenty-six pounds—and this on marines who were trained to a healthy leanness before ever entering battle!

Yet, despite fatigue, physical debilitation and the terrors of jungle warfare, the actual number of psychiatric casualties did not exceed—at a maximum—6 per cent of the total number of men evacuated from Guadalcanal! Since neither those with minor wounds or illnesses, nor those who died on the field are included among the evacuees, there is reason to believe that the mental casualties did not exceed 2 or 3 per cent of all casualties; less than a small fraction of 1 per cent of all the troops engaged on the island.

✦

Typical of the way in which increasing debilitation on the one hand and increasing strain on the other acted as upper and nether millstones was a case of the marine hospital corpsman, John Day.* Corpsman Day arrived at Guadalcanal, with the first wave, on August 7. His work, the rescue of the wounded, exposed him to action constantly and made him a special target for Jap snipers. Yet, for five weeks, he was no more frightened nor upset than the next man. In his own words, he was "too busy to be bothered."

About the middle of September, he began to experience headaches. Gradually they became more frequent and more severe. During the third week of September, while carrying a wounded man out of the line of fire, he felt something "snap in his back" between his shoulder blades. He completed his mission, although nauseated and dizzy. An examination at a first-aid station disclosed no physical lesion. From then on, though, he was increasingly conscious of his tiredness and "jumpiness," and his headaches increased in intensity. Yet entire days would pass in which he would not feel any pain and gave no thought to his condition.

On September 27, during an air raid, he began to shake and tremble so violently that his fellow corpsmen noticed his condition. He was sent to sick bay for two or three days and then evacuated from Guadalcanal by plane. On examination at the base hospital, he recalled two occasions on which shells landed within thirty yards of him. On one of these occasions he recollected being shaken up and dazed for a few hours, but he insisted that he had at no time fallen into unconsciousness.

Through all this period, Corpsman Day had been obsessed by a feeling that he had not succeeded in doing all he should have done for his fellow marines, although both the official

* For obvious reasons, this and all other names of psychiatric patients have been changed.

records and his own retelling of his history provide convincing evidence of exertions up to and far beyond the full call of duty.

When John Day reached the hospital, he was suffering from a large series of infected scratches and insect bites. His weight had fallen by twenty-two pounds! He had a marked nodding tremor of the head and the shaking of his hands was only accentuated with every attempt to control it. He was extremely sensitive to any excitement and especially to sharp noises, and noted in himself a marked difficulty in concentrating. He was particularly conscious of this because in school and college, he had always considered himself a good student, and had prided himself on his ability to concentrate well.

A few weeks later, after further evacuation to a hospital in New Zealand, John Day presented a radically different picture. His weight returned rapidly to normal. His skin infections were quickly cleared up, and with their passage he began to note in himself a gradual return towards normal reflexes. The head tremor disappeared and that of his hands occurred only during periods of excitement as, for example, at the beginning of psychiatric interviews. His sensitivity to noise persisted for some time longer and he found it difficult to be comfortable outside of the quiet hospital grounds. His incipient guilt complex was more difficult to overcome. But after a number of sessions with the hospital psychiatrist, even this feeling disappeared.

When I saw John Day, shortly before he returned to limited duty, he appeared at first glance to be a perfectly normal, healthy young man. As he talked and told his story, one could catch a slightly unnatural nervousness in his manner. When he lit a cigarette his hand shook a trifle. But he was obviously far on the road toward full recovery from his neurosis—having made almost as much progress in this direction as he had towards physical recovery.

The case of Corpsman Day is typical of perhaps 50 per cent of all the psycho-neurotic collapses which occurred on Guadalcanal. Under increasing strain and in a progressively weakened condition, he managed to perform his strenuous and hazardous duties for more than seven weeks. In the end, his breakdown proved to be what the doctors term psychosomatic, a physical collapse inducing marked mental symptoms. Prompt evacuation with the attendant complete change in both physical and mental environment soon restored his previous sound health.

Not every case, of course, is as simple nor as easily cured. Yet even the more severely broken men are capable of a rapid comeback under modern methods of treatment. Leon Herbert—a tall, thin, Virginia farm boy—was found on Guadalcanal wandering dazed through the coconut groves. Almost immediately after his rescue, he fell into a deep state of unconsciousness from which he did not emerge for four days. When he did awake he was unable to speak, and it was not until seven days after his evacuation that he first showed any awareness of his surroundings.

When he began to recover his speech, the doctors found him suffering from a pronounced amnesia. Not only did he have no recollection of his battle experience: when asked his name, he referred first to his dog-tag, and had to refer to it again when asked where he was from. Even the name of his home state bore no meaning for him, and he had no recollection of family or friends.

But as he lay in the hospital, his memory began to return in curious wispy patches. When shown a safety pin he recalled having seen such things before, and asked what they were used for. A watch excited his curiosity. He said he had seen one on the wrist, but never one like mine. Yet, he could name a pencil and remarked that mine was a "spiral-bound notebook."

The doctor who introduced me to Leon Herbert asked him about his religion. The boy looked at his dog-tag and said, "I suppose this 'P' means Protestant. I went to one of the services Sunday, but I didn't know what it was all about."

Confused and bewildered as he was by his surroundings, he still did not have to learn things after the manner of a child. Abilities came back to him in large gulps. The first time I saw him, he could name a book, but could not read any words. But a day later, after a single lesson, he was reading rapidly, although many familiar words impressed him as novel.

Although Leon Herbert's mental injury was far more severe than that of many another case, he, too, showed a rapid rate of recovery due, in part, to the promptness with which his condition was attacked and, in part, to the rapid physical recovery which he was able to achieve.

Nearly a third of all the cases which I saw were of the type classified by the doctors as "concussion syndrome"—men who had been rendered unconscious or dazed by a nearby explosion.

One such was MacAdams, a young marine sergeant who had spent nine years in the service before being sent to Guadalcanal. During all that time his record showed he had been a stable, normal individual. When I met him, in Auckland, he was awaiting his discharge back to duty. Though fully recovered he still retained a vivid recollection of his experiences.

"I went into Tulagi," he told me, "on August 7—the day it started. Then I was sent over to Guadalcanal. I fought hand-to-hand and had no troubles until September 22. That day a five-hundred-pound bomb blew me out of my foxhole and sprawled me on the ground. I don't think I was unconscious. I returned to my company and later—a day or two later—we'd captured two Jap howitzers and were dragging them back across the field. I became blind and I staggered and I had to lie down.

"I rested up for two days and then went back to duty. Then five days later I was out on patrol and when I came back to my foxhole I passed out completely. I thought it was due to the malaria but Doc up there, he said it was due to the concussion. I hadn't eaten anything for twelve days; couldn't hold my food and had no desire to eat. When they flew me out of there I'd lost forty-one pounds.

"Most of my troubles seemed to start a few days after the concussion. I began to get headaches—like my head was split open. Then I got the shakes. It was so bad I used to sit on my hands so people wouldn't see. And if you so much as snapped your fingers, bang—that set me off.

"At the hospital they fed me up and cured the malaria first. Then the doctors told me I shouldn't be holding in all the time. I used to hate to talk about it—what happened on Guadalcanal—but they told me it would do me good to talk. They explained things to me, clear.

"At first I thought it was the bunk. But after a couple of days—when I had these sessions with the doctors and when I talked with my buddies—it was a funny thing; my head stopped hurting. Then I began to have faith in them and I really tried to go along with the docs; to do whatever they said. And it got better all the time. It's like if you don't talk about it, you're going to dream about it instead. I used to have terrible dreams all the time and I'd wake up screaming. But after I got fleshed up and rested and I learned how to talk it out of me, the dreams just stopped.

"Then I came down to Auckland and, for a while, the

troubles came back. Like, for instance, I used to promise a fellow I'd meet him down town. Then I would forget about it. I would even forget who I'd promised it to. That would worry me because I thought I was really going nuts. So I had some more talks with the psychiatrist here. Those guys can sure talk to you. They explain things and make them clear. This doc, he showed me records of other men—how they had the same thing and got better. That gave me confidence again. The last four weeks I feel like a new man.

"I never been afraid of anything in my life before. But a month ago when they told me I was about ready to go back to duty—brother, I was scared stiff. The doc saw how scared I was and he said maybe I should stay here a while more. But last week I went in to see him and I told him I was ready now. And he said he was waiting for me, that he knew I'd come around."

Among the more difficult cases are those of men who develop a strange sense of guilt, a feeling of having betrayed the comrades they left at the scene of battle. One such man was Woodley, a Fire Controlman 2/Cl.—a slight, sharp-featured boy who sat shivering in a warm room as he told his story to a psychiatric officer in my presence.

"My ship, the ——— had been in nine actions and I had not felt any special nervousness. On November 30, at 11 P.M., when we were at ———, we got orders to go to Guadalcanal to intercept the Tokyo Express. Their destroyers launched torpedoes and our heavy cruisers opened up and returned the Jap fire. We were getting good results until the ——— started to burn and we had to cross her so that the other ships were silhouetted in her glare. Then we 'caught fish.'

"The tension among the director crew had been strong. The torpedo struck right below us and oil and fire had been thrown up the fire control tower. As soon as the blaze burst upward, everybody became panicky and we all rushed into the plotting room. Then we realized that it had no other exit . . . it was a trap we had walked into.

"I hollered, 'Let's get out' and the chief and myself and one officer went back to the fire control station. The port side was burning and the ladder had been blown away. The officer said, 'I've lost all hope.' He asked for his pistol but the chief wouldn't give it to him. Then he just lay down in the oil and gave up. That's what he said, 'I give up' . . . just like that.

"I began to think there might be some way out by going up the mast. I didn't know but it looked like it was worth a chance. I tried to get the officer to get up and follow me . . . but he wouldn't move . . . just lay there waiting for the flames to cook him. Then one man came running out of the plotting room and jumped the shield. I looked over, because it seemed like maybe he was going to make the water that way. But I saw him go straight into the hole in the deck, right into the flames. I started up the ladder then and undogged the hatch and got the cover open. I must have gotten halfway through when I passed out because the next thing I remember was I was being lowered down over the starboard side with a rope.

"After a few hours I began to worry about my mates. That's when this guilty feeling the doctor has been telling me about must have started. I know when I talk to you that I did the best I could. But at night I get these dreams . . . I dream the whole battle over and over again and I wake up screaming because I let my buddies down."

Such feelings of guilt are viewed by most psychiatrists as more complex manifestations of "combat fatigue" or "war neurosis." Men showing the slightest tendency towards the development of these obsessions are carefully watched. The feeling itself is counteracted by detailed explanations of the situation in interviews between the doctor and the patient. This treatment is further fortified by free contact with non-psychiatric cases through which the mental patient learns that he is not held in disrepute by his fellow men. Often those who develop feelings of guilt are among the most conscientious and devoted men in the service. Once treatment has relieved them of their obsession, they are usually able to return to duty. Many of them return stronger and better men despite—or possibly even because of—their experiences.

In treating such cases, psychiatrists in the South Pacific have learned much. Perhaps most important of all the things they have learned is that war's mental casualties are not as bad as they had anticipated. In part, the psychiatrists ascribe this hopeful situation to the effectiveness of the psychiatric tests by which unstable individuals or those with a predisposition towards mental collapse are eliminated from the service or placed in non-combat positions.

In one series of four hundred cases which came before the psychiatrists, only seventeen—less than 5 per cent—had shown symptoms, prior to their exposure to battle, which might have served as a warning signal to the examining psychiatrists. Nor were these all clear-cut cases. They represent rather those border-line symptoms which are noted only after collapse makes their previous significance obvious. Even this 5 per cent of supposedly predictable breakdowns looms large only in comparison with the total number of breakdown cases. When assessed, however, against the entire number of troops subjected to combat conditions, it becomes apparent that only a rare and occasional case is now slipping through the successive psychiatric screens.

A second conclusion—in which most if not all psychiatrists in the field now concur—concerns the effect of adequate indoctrination in holding down the number of mental casualties. A large proportion of such casualties represent the attempt of the mind to find escape from a situation which has become unbearable to it. This manifests itself in many different ways. Some men show marked hysterical reactions such as paralysis, facial tics, loss of the power of speech, and partial or total amnesia. Others demonstrate the desire for escape more frankly through crying spells and similar manifestations.

Indoctrination into an understanding of the necessity and the importance of the battle can here serve to make otherwise unbearable situations tolerable. In the Marine Corps, all men receive a substantial quantity of such training. But of all Marine units, the Raiders are perhaps most carefully selected and trained to have a full understanding of their part in the war, of the rightness of their cause, and of the importance of the sacrifices which they are asked to make.

The effect of this training has shown itself in the low incidence of mental casualties among such troops, despite the adverse conditions under which they operate. This was particularly notable on Guadalcanal, where one Raider battalion made a thirty-day march through enemy held territory in which individual units of troops frequently operated for long periods completely on their own. Such men were naturally subjected, to an even greater degree than any others, to the terror caused by Jap tactics. Yet their training and their indoctrination held war neurosis down to a minimum. In more than six hundred records of mental casualties which I examined—from Guadalcanal and elsewhere—I recall only one which could be assessed against this unit!

Of equal importance in the prevention of mental casualties is training and experience in the particular type of warfare to which troops will be subjected in battle. On Guadalcanal, battle conditions turned out to be far different from those which had originally been envisioned when the participating troops received their training. An amphibious force, which had been trained for the capture and short-time occupation of a beach-head, found itself in what amounted to a long-term siege defense. In the first days of battle, when the men were still expecting early relief, mental casualties were few. In the last two weeks of August and the first two weeks of September such cases came into one base hospital from Guadalcanal at a rate of only five or six a week. But in the week of September 15, the number jumped to ten and in the following week to fifteen. It hovered around this figure until October 21, when it rose to thirty-two. The first week in November saw thirty-four mental cases coming into this hospital. The next week saw twenty-five, and after that the number dropped off until by December 15, it had fallen back to an average of eight per week.

The curve followed by these cases closely paralleled the action on the island. It remained low during the initial period of rapid success in attaining first objectives. It rose when the battles increased in intensity, and as it became apparent to the men that relief would be a long time in coming. But in the middle of November, although the struggle itself did not diminish in violence, new troops were beginning to come in in substantial numbers. From then on, mental casualties dropped off.

In part, these figures reflected a substantial improvement in the quality and quantity of food, shelter, and supplies. Military men would, no doubt, place substantial emphasis upon these latter factors, but many a psychiatrist—and particularly those who have seen and treated these casualties—will feel that a major cause of the sharp rise which occurred during the middle period of the battle was to be found in the feeling of the men that they were engaged in a struggle very different from that for which they had prepared themselves. Once they had become accustomed to jungle warfare and to the tactics of the Japanese, the element of terror lost much of its potency.

A final conclusion, arising directly from the experiences of Guadalcanal, concerns the factor of duration of battle exposure. Very few of the mental casualties which occurred at any time during the battle were found to affect men who had been in combat less than four weeks. The vast majority of the mental casualties were incurred between the fourth and seventh weeks in combat. Curiously enough, those who passed through seven weeks unscathed almost never turned up as mental cases.

All of these conclusions lie within the realm of what might be called preventive psychiatry. It is interesting to note that our more recent battles in the Solomons seem to indicate that the military men are fully aware of the implications of the psychiatric experiences arising from Guadalcanal and have taken steps to so plan future actions as to eliminate many of the factors making for a high mental casualty rate.

No doubt, much of their change in tactics arises from purely military rather than medical considerations. Yet, wherever I have traveled through the South Pacific, I have seen the military men ready to consider medical problems as an essential and even a basic factor in any evaluation of the military situation.

On Guadalcanal, it was judged necessary to make the first attack upon the island's airfield. This was essential for we possessed no other airfields within close flying range. But it had the effect of leaving the Japs the entire island to maneuver in while penning our own troops into a narrow area. In contrast, the attacks on Lae and Salamaua, in New Guinea, and upon Munda, on New Georgia Island, reversed this procedure. Our forces retained the wide field of maneuver and the Japanese were penned into an ever-narrowing area around their airfields.

The greater experience of our now well-seasoned troops has served in these actions to minimize psychiatric casualties. But their ability to obtain relief after a period of exposure to battle—an ability inherently absent at Guadalcanal and carefully provided through the new tactics—undoubtedly is playing an important part in reducing the incidence of mental breakdowns.

While preventive psychiatry can do much to minimize mental casualties it cannot hope to eliminate all. No matter how many the safeguards, war will still subject men to strains of far greater intensity and duration than those of normal life. But here again, Guadalcanal has confirmed and fortified theories which psychiatrists had begun to put into practice even before the start of the war.

In the last war, the psychiatric casualty had to run a gauntlet of derision and skepticism during the period in which he showed the early signs of collapse. His own comrades were trained to look upon him as a malingerer. Company and regimental doctors frequently took the same view. Even the psychiatrists themselves felt obliged to view all but the frankest cases of mental illness with at least some skepticism.

Since that time, a great change has come over the views of both the medical profession and the average citizen. Among the men who had seen action on Guadalcanal, there was no disposition to look upon the mental casualty as a "gold brick." On the contrary, the men became extremely sensitive in their ability to recognize the symptoms of incipient crack-ups. Frequently, enlisted men and officers spot such cases in their early stages, long before the harassed doctors would have noted them.

The average company doctor in the Marines and the ship's doctors in the Navy are far more familiar with psychiatry today than general practitioners have ever been before. Those who have come from civil life have had at least a smattering of the psychiatric knowledge which their fathers, a generation ago, lacked. All have been taught—as part of their naval training—how to recognize and how to treat psychiatric casualties before they reach an advanced stage of development. Psychiatrists have, in fact, made the unexpected complaint that cases are sometimes referred to them at so early a stage of mental degeneration that the classic symptoms do not yet show up clearly.

For both the psychiatrist and the mentally injured man, this changed attitude has been a great boon. It has made possible, in many cases, the early treatment of conditions which would otherwise develop into a state far less likely of a successful cure. Early diagnosis has undoubtedly played a large part in making for the high rate of rapid recoveries achieved at the naval hospitals in the South Pacific.

Coupled with early diagnosis and early evacuation is the promptest possible definitive treatment. The first rule, which psychiatrists everywhere in the South Pacific seem to recognize, is that such cases need rest more than anything else. Worn and worried, these men find it difficult and often impossible to gain any sleep until they drop from sheer exhaustion. Others, when they finally fall asleep, wake shortly with frightening nightmares. The doctor's first step, therefore, is to put the patient to sleep. Using such drugs as phenobarbitol or sodium amytal, they frequently provide the incoming patient with as much as forty-eight hours of continuous sleep.

From such sleep the men awake greatly refreshed. Their more noticeable physical symptoms—such as violent jerking motions or continuous shivering—often disappear with a single treatment.

Rest is followed by emotional desensitization. The patients are encouraged to tell of their combat experiences, both to

the doctors and to each other. At times this produces temporary periods of excitement, but almost invariably it results
in definite gains for the patient. The men soon feel, as
MacAdams did, that the doctors "can do things" for them.
They overcome their original shyness and find catharsis in
their ability to repeat their stories to sympathetic ears.

In a few cases, at Base Dash, convulsive shock therapy was
used. Lieutenant Commander James A. Sagebiel showed me
the records of three cases in which he used the drug Metra-
zole to induce a convulsion which rendered his patients symp-
tom free. The drug is a violent one and must be used with
great care under controlled conditions. For this reason it is
not utilized in most cases—other methods achieve adequate
results although they may take somewhat longer to effect a
cure.

In still other instances pentathol sodium—a drug more
frequently used as a surgical anaesthetic—is injected into a
vein to produce hypnosis. Under the influences of this drug
men, who could not tell their stories clearly under any other
circumstances, find it possible to relive their battle memories
and to talk about them. Deeply buried emotional conflicts
come to the surface at such times and aid the doctors toward
that basic understanding of each case which is essential in the
achievement of a cure. The talking the patient does while
under the influence of the drug goes a long way, of itself,
toward effecting a cure. The things a man says under hypnosis often provide doctors with a lead for further, un-
hypnotized discussions which usually serve to complete the
cure within a few days.

It is hazardous to cite any statistics in respect to psychiatric
casualties for they naturally vary greatly from zone to zone
and from time to time. Yet from my own observations—
interviewing several score of men in various stages of recov-

ery and in examining the records of many hundreds of such cases—several conclusions seem self-evident:

Of men actually in combat, far fewer than one-half of 1 per cent will show any mental symptoms necessitating hospitalization except under the most exceptional circumstances.

Of those diagnosed as mental patients, only a very few will be psychotics—suffering from dementia praecox, delusions of grandeur, schizophrenia, or similar pronounced insanities. Invariably, these will be men who were well on the road to such troubles before enlistment—who would, in fact, have succumbed to these manifestations of mental disease in peace as well as war.

The vast majority of mental difficulties will be situational neuroses clearing up rapidly once the pressure is released and the situation changed.

Finally, by far the overwhelming number of these men will return to duty. A substantial proportion go back to full combat duty; a larger number remain in the armed services, but are wisely given limited duties usually outside battle zones. Only a very few of those mental cases which are not coupled with a physical injury will have to be discharged from the armed forces. And even of these a substantial proportion will effect a suitable adjustment in civil life and will not require endless hospitalization.

I went into the South Pacific expecting to find Navy doctors particularly successful in those fields in which drugs or surgery can serve to cure a man. But I think I was like most Americans—and many psychiatrists, too—in my expectation of seeing many a man wrecked mentally by combat, and incurable.

I did see many mental cases, though far fewer than sensational headlines had led me to expect. But the vast majority of those I saw were men who had already recovered from their difficulties. Beyond all the other hopeful facts that came to my attention, this—I think—is the most cheering development that has come out of South Pacific medicine. For the psychiatrists are winning *their* war—more completely than even the most sanguine among them had ever dared to hope.

CHAPTER XIII

THE LONG VOYAGE HOME

SHE was a Dutch freighter, built for the Java trade. Even her gray war paint could not entirely hide the beauty of her sharp lines. But if she had been some rusty old tub she would still have looked gloriously, bewitchingly beautiful to us, for her destination was home.

I came aboard early and, for a day, I was away from the sights of war. The Dutch officers who manned the ship treated me to a private cabin, a private bath and a fabulous dinner, topped by an even more fabulous toast, which we drank in Bols gin. The American contingent on board—a gunnery officer, a communicator and two doctors—were men fresh from home. They talked of the new ration books and the shortage of gasoline, of plays I had never seen and movies whose names I had never heard. I sat back in a soft chair and drank it in, anticipating in advance the joys of getting home, like a connoisseur who rolls a drop of fine cognac, carefully, on his tongue before swallowing it.

The next morning our ship changed. Out across the harbor came self-propelled barges, loaded down with barracks bags and sea chests. They were followed by other barges bearing a human cargo, five hundred men in a motley array of uniforms—Marine greens, Navy blues and the sun-bleached khakis of the Army. Some men raced up the ladders easily. Others held the line back as they puffed their way slowly up each painful step. And many stumbled up on crutches or on casts while the winches went over the side to bring a few aboard on stretchers. But hale or haggard, every face was smiling and every eye glistened. As they milled around on the now densely crowded decks, one could be certain that nowhere on board was there a man who regretted leaving the tropics; for none could the anchor be raised too soon.

Our spacious, empty ship was roomy no more. In the cabins designed for twelve peacetime passengers we now crowded seventy-five officers. In the hull, the great compartments were filled, four tiers high, with enlisted men arranging their gear on their pipe-and-canvas bunks. The decks, fore and aft, were crowded by day and far into the night with men drinking in the sun and the quiet or enjoying a cool and restful sleep in the tropic evening.

But as long as we could hear the turbines singing down below, as long as the foam rushed by along side, no one cared if he had to stand in line for meals. We were jam-packed and rubbing up against each other but it didn't matter, for we were going home.

That first morning the ship was organized. Mixed crews from every service took up K. P. details or anti-submarine watches. But after all the work that could be invented had been divided up, each man found nine-tenths of his day still gloriously his own.

I shared my "private" room now with twenty-two officers. From dawn until far into the night my "private" shower was occupied by men who couldn't seem to get their fill of the pleasure of bathing in warm water—with real soap and a fresh towel. Long before our turn came, we stood outside the wardroom and waited for our chance to sit down before the rich Dutch food. It wasn't until a week after we left Noumea that any man stopped taking two oranges—fresh with their California wrappers—from the bowl that stood at the wardroom exit. In the intervals between meals we treated each other to all the beer we could buy, drinking it straight from the cold and dewy bottles that came in an endless stream from the galley's roomy iceboxes. It was an orgy of self-indulgence in which every man wallowed, as was his right, until some of us grew fat and all of us grew lazy.

But after we finished with our duties—the sacred, joyous duties of eating, drinking, and sleeping like free men for a change—we still found time to sit around and talk. At first the talk was all of home. By tacit agreement we barred the South Pacific from our minds, forgot the war and spent our days in reminiscences or in making plans. But after the first week the talk changed. We were far enough out by then to think of our stay on the islands as something safely in the past. We lay in the sun on the broad decks or in the crowded comfort of our cabins and told each other stories of the men we had known and the battles we had seen. Men talked freely—far more so than they would have if they were all officers of a single unit. For now, detached from their outfits, all men were equal, all were veterans—whether of the office battles in Noumea or the jungle conflicts of Guadalcanal.

Down on the main deck and in the holds among the enlisted men I could watch the same process going on for, as a correspondent without rank, I was accepted equally among both groups. Gradually, as the days passed, our five hundred evacuees split up along new lines. There were the casualties, the men who were on their way to further hospitalization in the States—perhaps to an early discharge. Others, uninjured, were returning "for new construction"—anticipating a thirty-day leave before they joined a new vessel and went to sea again. Still others, a closely knit group, were the survivors of a wrecked destroyer.

These last were always together and always just a little apart from the rest. Their conversation was all of their own ship, the fine ship that was no more, the ship that had gone through the battle of Savo Island and tangled with a Jap battleship and sunk a Jap cruiser and polished off two Jap destroyers. They never tired of telling how their ship had taken nine direct hits, including three from the fourteen-inch guns of a battleship. They talked less of the other engagement, the later battle in which they lost their ship and half their crew. But even when this battle was discussed, the trim destroyer was never spoken of as a dead thing. To these men it still lived, it still was home.

The destroyer's crew—officers and men—dreamed of a thirty-day leave. But mostly they hoped for a new assignment to a new destroyer that would bear the same old name. It was a dream that many of them knew would never come true. For the Navy has found it best to separate such crews of survivors, crews which have achieved so great a unity among themselves that newcomers are accepted with only the greatest difficulty into the veterans' circle. They knew that they would probably be split up to share their invaluable experience among a dozen new ships. But until that moment came, they chose to live with a dream and to cling together, to their memory of life as a fighting team.

Among our seventy-five officers were half a dozen doctors. Their time, too, was spent in reminiscences and in comparisons—in endless arguments between the Army and the Navy. But, after the first few days, the habits of physicians reasserted themselves. One by one they gravitated to the sick bay to look over the patients in the hold and to help the duty doctors, Lieutenant Commander Greer and Lieutenant Kitchen, in their treatment of these men.

There wasn't much for them to do, for the patients on board were well taken care of. Most of the men were far advanced in their convalescence and required little attention.

But what there was for the volunteer doctors to do they did willingly, feeling it important to keep their hands in practice and unable to forget that—in uniform or out—they were still physicians.

Our casualties were a mixed group. Some were men, wasted by disease, on whom clothes hung only to emphasize the sharpness of their bones and the thinness of their flesh. Others walked the deck on crutches, favoring their game legs but anxious to keep moving as if they had to prove to themselves that they were able to get around unaided. A few were very sick—men who were destined for a long stay at some great naval hospital ashore and, probably, for eventual discharge from the service.

It was these last who aroused the pity and the indignation of the officers in the passenger quarters under the bridge. One day—about a week after we had put to sea—a Marine colonel wandered down to the sick bay. While he was down there the daily boat drill whistle blew and the familiar Dutch voice came over the loudspeakers saying, "Der drill is vor der tr-r-oops oonly." The colonel watched the injured men as they clambered out of their bunks and made their way painfully up the ladders to their boat stations. And he came up to the officers' lounge seething with indignation. He borrowed my typewriter and tapped out a memorandum. Then he passed among the officers to get signatures for his round robin. The note was an offer to give up our bunks, to exchange places with the casualties in the sick bay. And almost every officer aboard took up the colonel's indignation and willingly signed the sheet.

But while the officers—thinking now only as civilians and as Americans—discussed the apparent wrong and planned to right it—while all this went on—one of the doctors appeared in the room. Quietly and patiently he explained the needs of the men in the sick bay. He showed us how much better off they were down there, where they could be watched by the corpsmen and given every attention, than they would be amidst the noise and crowding of our cabins. In the end the colonel folded up his memorandum and quietly dropped it over the side.

It was a minor incident, a small misunderstanding in which the colonel and all the rest of the non-medical men were in the wrong. But it demonstrated once again—if any demonstration were needed—the attitude of deep consideration for the wounded which exists among all the men in the South Pacific. Even the old regulars—and the colonel *was* a regular, long accustomed to the distinctions of rank—even they wanted no seeming privileges at the expense of any man who had borne a wound.

It was towards the end of our second week at sea, after we had crossed the equator again and were heading northward toward the west coast, that I turned to the notes I had kept for all the months since first I joined the *Relief*. Now at last, with the Solomons five thousand miles behind, I could view these notes as something more than a day-to-day record. Distance lent them perspective and, as I turned the pages on the sunny deck, I got a new picture of Navy medicine.

I had left the States expecting to find the Navy efficient and capable in its treatment of the sick and wounded. I had found efficiency—and an extremely high degree of competence—at all the hospitals from Auckland to the Russells.

But I had found much more than that. I knew now that the Navy Medical Corps had won victories quite as great and quite as important as any that are won with cannon. I knew now that never in all history before had the men of any armed force been so well protected against death and disease, so well cared for when sick or injured. I knew, too, how this victory had been won, in a series of unnoticed, unpublicized battles fought by doctors and nurses—and by the enlisted men of the hospital corps—on every ship and every festering tropic island. Most of all, I had come to see this phase of war as something more than a matter of equipment and statistics. For all the planning and all the thousands of tons of supplies—the x-rays and the stethoscopes, the scalpels and the drugs—all these alone never saved a wounded man or cured a victim of malaria. The real victory of Navy medicine—the victory that has to be won all over again with every new battle—is achieved by a host of selfless men whose military uniforms can never hide the fact that, above all things, they are doctors.

Even as I read my notes I could see all around me the amazing results of their work—the men with bright faces and happy smiles who were going home now, the men who, but for our doctors in uniform, would lie rotting beneath the soil of some plague-swept South Sea island. Each seaman and doughboy who lolled before me in his shorts, tanning himself beneath the tropic sun, was a living tribute to these men. I found myself wishing that people at home—the worried mothers, the lonely wives—could somehow see them as I saw them now; could somehow know that much of the terror has been taken out of this horrible thing called war, that America knew not only how to destroy but how to rebuild as well.

It was perhaps because I viewed things in such a light during the last few days of our long journey home, that our entry into San Francisco proved a great and disappointing anti-climax. I had pictured it as somewhat like our entry into Auckland—but magnified and enhanced a hundredfold, as befits homecoming heroes. Somehow I expected—although I knew it couldn't be—that people would turn out to wave at us as we came through the Golden Gate, that a band would play and girls with flowers would line the dock. Most of the men expected something of the sort, though none of us put it into words.

Instead, we passed under the bridge and moved slowly up to our dock unnoticed, just another gray ship coming out of a gray and foggy sea. Even the sun failed to greet us when we returned to our homeland. The trains rolled across the bridges and the busy ferries carried their busy war workers to Oakland and the ship yards. The tugs pushed past us in the busy harbor and their whistles shouted merely, "Make way, make passage." We moved up to our berth unmarked and unwelcomed.

Behind the gray iron that sheathed the pier were long rows of ambulances—khaki ones from the Army hospitals and gray and blue ones from the Navy. The men filed down the gangplanks and entered the waiting cars and were quietly carried away beyond the dock. On the Embarcadero, the ambulances merged with and were lost among the trucks and taxis of San Francisco.

America had no greeting for its casualties. But the Navy was taking care of its own.

THE END